Foundations for
health service
management

OCCASIONAL HUNDREDS
3

Foundations for health service management

A Scicon report for the Scottish Home and Health
Department on the requirements for
a health service information system

By K. E. Bodenham and F. Wellman
of Scientific Control Systems Ltd

With a Foreword by
Gordon McLachlan

Published for
The Nuffield Provincial
Hospitals Trust by the
Oxford University Press
London New York Toronto
1972

Oxford University Press, Ely House, London W1
Glasgow New York Toronto Melbourne Wellington
Cape Town Salisbury Ibadan Nairobi Dar es Salaam Lusaka Addis Ababa
Bombay Calcutta Madras Karachi Lahore Dacca
Kuala Lumpur Singapore Hong Kong Tokyo

ISBN 0 19 721369 3

Designed by Bernard Crossland

Printed in Great Britain by
FinaPrint (Printers) Ltd, Oxford

NOTE

Although this study was commissioned by the Scottish Home and Health Department it should be noted that the authors are responsible for the accuracy of the observations and the recommendations made

Contents

Foreword

Unlike the previous report by Scientific Control Systems Ltd, *Focus on Medical Computer Development*, the study, of which this is the report, was not commissioned by the Trust but directly by the Scottish Home and Health Department. Like its predecessor from Scicon it has, however, lessons which are applicable to other parts of the UK. Without labouring those which are explicitly stated or can be got by analogy—and there are many in the report for those who want to see—there are probably two important lessons which are implicit.

The first is that this conscious effort on the part of a major government department to seek outside expert advice to determine what management needs are, in order to fulfil its objectives, must also be seen against the fact that it is related in time to the restructuring of the NHS in a part of the UK which, because possibly of its size, has shown a liveliness of approach which promises some flexibility in experiment. Consequently, if there is any validity in the conclusions reached there must surely be a strong case for some of the proposed reforms being put in hand at the same time as any reconstruction is being carried out. To wait until the new structure is built would seem a prescription to prolong the dislocation period following the passage of new legislation. The case for a package-deal in which as many changes as possible are effected is strong.

Perhaps equally important, however, is that one is struck once more by the absolute necessity for management in this highly complex conglomeration of personal services to secure relevant up-to-date information if they are to be effective and efficacious, as well as efficient. Yet the whole fabric of management intelligence concerning needs and priorities depends on the collation of information concerning individuals on aspects of illness of patients related to their environment, families, and so on, much of which information in any case has to be collected to meet the requirements of clinical medicine for diagnosis and therapy. But because of the current understandable sensitivity to possible breaches of confidentiality, it is not inconceivable that intolerable restrictions may be imposed which could seriously hinder the collation of information. That this would be a tragedy cannot be doubted. This information, as the advances in epidemiology have shown, can be helpful not only to the treatment of individual patients but also lead to a better knowledge of the natural history of diseases and their impact on certain identifiable groups. It is also clear, however, that such hindrance will be prejudicial to the efficient operation of health services and if the Government is really serious in its emphasis on improved management of the NHS, it should take note of the position. Hitherto the voices raised against the availability and linking of information have tended to have it all their own way, reflecting the public concern at the possibility of breaches of confidentiality. Surely there must be an attempt to assess the position coolly, constructing as necessary, appropriate safeguards against abuse of information gathered for clinical and social purposes. It is certainly time a sober debate was started on the general subject, and experiments were conceived, designed to see how far it is possible to safeguard privacy while at the same time making available suitable information not only to clinicians but also to managers; for like the epidemiologists information is the raw material of the manager's professional activities.

It would seem desirable—and this is the Trust's interest in this particular publication—that this penetrating report on the requirements of a basic information system should be debated at length in order to ensure that at the time of structural change some of the very necessary requirements at local levels can be incorporated in the schemes developed to ensure that health services can, in the future, be effectively managed. Without such fundamental elements it seems useless to stress the need for better management.

GORDON McLACHLAN

Acknowledgements

Many individuals and groups have contributed to the contents of this report. A list of those consulted is given in Appendix B and we should like to thank them all for so readily giving up their time to discuss the problems of the future with us. Many of them provided useful written material.

In particular we should like to thank first the Research and Intelligence Unit of the Scottish Home and Health Department, especially Mr D. D. Rose, for their help in making all the arrangements and appointments which were necessary, and secondly our colleagues in Scicon, especially Mr J. M. Ockenden (Managing Director) and Dr S. H. Storey, whose general guidance and detailed critical comment over an extended period have proved invaluable.

K.E.B. and F W.

1. Introduction

Scientific Control Systems Ltd were commissioned by the Scottish Home
and Health Department in the autumn of 1970 to undertake a preliminary
study of requirements of a managerial and administrative data system for an
integrated health service. After agreeing terms of reference, a copy of which
is provided as Appendix A, the study began on 1 November 1970. It has
covered a very wide range of activities, and the chief aim has been to identify
more closely the areas of data deserving special attention and the problems
which will have to be overcome if a viable system is to be established. The
report, after the brief summary of recommendations which follows this introduction, deals first with the questions of organization and objectives
(Chapter 3), then with actual data requirements for an integrated service
(Chapters 4-10) and finally with the major development problems to which
in our opinion concerted effort will have to be applied, beginning with questions of general organization of information services (Chapter 11) and ending
with detailed staffing and cost considerations (Chapter 17).

Although health service systems will make increasing use of computers, the
report avoids specific mention of them wherever possible. The availability
and versatility of computers will inevitably affect systems philosophy but computers should permit, rather than cause, the operation of systems. In a service
environment, with keen competition for resources, the cost of systems must
always be measured against their potential value, and this applies to computer
systems as to any others.

The study has been undertaken against a background of increasing public
concern over the question of databanks and confidentiality of data. There
have been conferences, repeated questions in Parliament, and statements and
mis-statements in the Press on this subject while the decennial census aroused
misgivings in many people. We believe that medical databanks should and can
be kept quite separate from other databanks, and that the problems of
security and confidentiality can be overcome. Chapter 15 deals with this issue
as one of the problems which will have to be solved.

The proposed reorganization, set out in the White Paper (2), affords great
opportunities for rationalization of health services and optimisation of the
service provided to the public. We hope our recommendations will provide a
basis from which the National Health Service can develop the information
systems essential to the provision of such services.

2. Summary of major conclusions and recommendations

1. The focal points of managerial and administrative activity and responsibility will be a number (probably fourteen) of health boards and a number of central bodies (probably the Scottish Home and Health Department (SHHD), Scottish Health Services Planning Council (SHSPC), and Common Services Agency (CSA)). Health boards and the central bodies will therefore require information on which to base decisions relating to operational activities and strategic planning. As health boards are to provide services to the population they should have first-level data relating to that population. The central authorities, who will be concerned more with strategy and objectives, are more likely to need access to summarized data, supplemented by the facility to call up more detailed data when required (Chapters 3 and 4).

2. Major areas of data identified are patient data, personnel, supplies, drugs, and buildings. The collection and use of data on these subjects should be put on an organized footing (Chapters 5-9).

3. The establishment of a basic register of the people in each area, to which can be linked such activities as hospital discharges, immunization programmes, and notification of special disabilities or risks, should be regarded as of major importance (Chapter 5).

4. There seems to be no reason why the General Register Office (GRO) should not continue to maintain the National Health Service Central Register (NHSCR) (Chapter 5).

5. A personnel management function would be able to develop its own tailor-made personnel information system, based on a personnel databank, covering the activities of recruitment, appointment, promotion, pay and conditions of service, payroll and superannuation, and manpower planning (Chapter 6).

6. Data on supplies, including prices, suppliers, and consumption at all levels, is required if the central supplies organization recommended by the recent working party (10) is to be fully effective (Chapter 7).

7. Prescription pricing and analysis by computer should be reconsidered: a preliminary study will be required of possible implementation methods (Chapter 8).

8. Buildings and plant are long-term investments needing careful evaluation. Accounting practices should enable the required data to be provided to planning groups (Chapter 9).

9. There are a number of subsidiary databanks whose relationships to the major systems need to be considered (Chapter 10).

10. The important function of information services would be most effective if established as an all-Scotland function (Chapter 11).

3   Summary of major conclusions and recommendations

11. The information services should include the NHS's own data-processing function and the NHS should not be dependent on Scottish Office Computer Service (SOCS) for this activity (Chapter 11).

12. If data is to be made accessible, it must be collected and stored as a series of readily retrievable items, and the collection of statistics from the bottom level of the service should be discontinued as soon as and as far as possible (Chapter 11).

13. The first steps towards development of a data system should be taken now if any part of the system is to be operational by 1 April 1974, the date provisionally fixed for establishment of the new organization. Responsibility for each development should be specifically allocated (Chapter 12).

14. It would be helpful if a standard identification number (preferably the NHS number) were to be used for all purposes (Chapter 13).

15. Questions of security and confidentiality need to be examined rationally. Establishment of a code of practice would be helpful (Chapter 14).

16. A greater measure of standardization should be sought, particularly in the areas of software and application development, clerical procedures, and record formats (Chapter 15).

17. The cheapest and most effective method of data capture must be used for each environment (Chapter 16).

18. Development of data systems would best be entrusted to a professionally staffed information services group which could co-ordinate developments both centrally and at the periphery. Multidisciplinary teams would be an effective way of ensuring the practicality of developments (Chapter 17).

19. Costs of an information service will be more than compensated for by savings and improvements in the service provided (Chapter 17).

3. Organization and objectives of the health service

The Green Paper (1) published in December 1968 outlined a system involving a single-tier structure for the integrated health service with a number of area health authorities, each responsible for the provision of total medical care within a geographical area. It was recognized that some support services would be more economically or efficiently provided from a Common Services Agency, for example, legal services, architectural and engineering services, the blood transfusion service, and information services.

Since 1968 wide-ranging discussions have been held between the various NHS organizations and the SHHD to examine the outline suggestions and to evolve a satisfactory operational organization. A White Paper (2) has now been published, taking account of these discussions and indicating firm proposals for the future organization of the NHS.

While much of the detail has still to be decided, it now seems probable that health boards will be established to administer all health service functions at local level and that responsibility for general planning and policy matters will be vested in bodies to be established centrally with ultimate over-all responsibility resting with the Secretary of State and the SHHD. In order to examine information requirements rationally, it is necessary to identify the functional activities of these local and central bodies.

Fig. 3.1 illustrates the differences between present and future organizational structure, and indicates the necessity to identify functions and develop techniques now, so that the new structure will be placed on firm foundations from its inception.

3.1. Health boards

Each health board will provide the services now provided separately by regional hospital boards, executive councils, and local health authorities, plus the school health and dental services.

Identification and planning of the detailed work which is implicit in the provision of these services has not yet begun. The major services and the resources available to provide the services are:

Services
Maternity, geriatrics, screening for presymptomatic disease, primary care, preventive services, developmental paediatrics, monitoring of known risk groups, accident services, hospital services.

Resources
Staff, equipment, supplies, buildings, transport, drugs.

The health board will need to shape its services so as to take into account many different kinds of local variations of which the following are among the most obvious: geography (highland, lowland, seaside, inland); industry (pollution, motorway hazards); age distribution (new town, retirement locality).

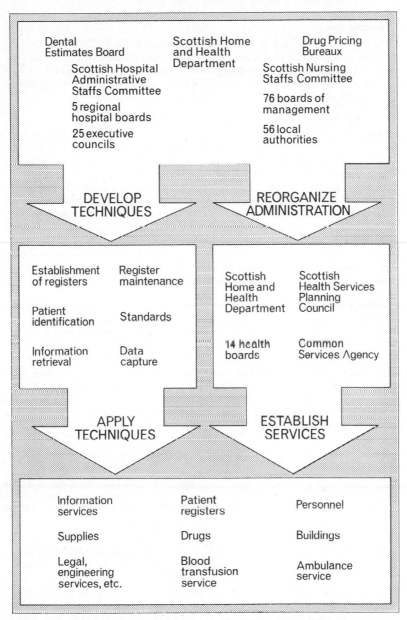

Dental Estimates Board

Scottish Hospital Administrative Staffs Committee

5 regional hospital boards

25 executive councils

Scottish Home and Health Department

Drug Pricing Bureaux

Scottish Nursing Staffs Committee

76 boards of management

56 local authorities

DEVELOP TECHNIQUES

REORGANIZE ADMINISTRATION

Establishment of registers

Register maintenance

Patient identification

Standards

Information retrieval

Data capture

Scottish Home and Health Department

14 health boards

Scottish Health Services Planning Council

Common Services Agency

APPLY TECHNIQUES

ESTABLISH SERVICES

Information services

Patient registers

Personnel

Supplies

Drugs

Buildings

Legal, engineering services, etc.

Blood transfusion service

Ambulance service

Fig. 3.1. Development and reorganization in the National Health Service

7

3.2. Central roles

Each health board will act as the agent of the Secretary of State and be financially accountable to the SHHD. It is therefore essential to define central roles clearly at an early stage so that there can be no subsequent confusion over delineation of authority. The three major roles are policy, planning, and service.

3.2.1. *Policy and planning*

This can take two forms. First, it will be necessary to deal with Acts of Parliament, such as the Abortion Act, to interpret them and to make provision for them. For example, costs incurred as a result of the Abortion Act have had to be met out of a fixed NHS vote.

Secondly, policy can be recommended by planning groups but care will need to be exercised over the costing of recommendations and close liaison will need to be maintained with those responsible for financial control.

Suitable arrangements will be required so that broad policy decisions can be turned into detailed plans for implementation at all levels of NHS. This will call for close working co-ordination between the health boards and the central organization and in addition will require consultation with those responsible for such matters as medical education and medical research.

3.2.2. *Service*

It now seems clear that a Common Services Agency will be established. The precise form which this will take has not been decided but the degree of central influence over individual functions must be tailored to the requirements of the functions themselves. In some cases, therefore, a complete specialist service will be provided, in others an advisory service, while in still others the centre could primarily be concerned with the setting of standards. Finally, it seems that for reasons of efficiency detailed operational working will be carried out centrally in some cases. Examples of the various levels are as follows:

Special services

These are the services first mentioned in the 1968 Green Paper, for instance legal, architectural, and engineering. It would hardly make sense for each health board to hire its own highly qualified staff if it can make use of a well-organized central function. Local hiring of such personnel would be extremely expensive, would make it more difficult to attract the right calibre of person and could lead to under-utilization of the staff.

Detailed operations

There are a number of routine operations which could most efficiently be carried out by a central body. Three of these have been recognized already and are currently carried out by the Dental Estimates Board, the Drug Pricing Bureaux, and the Superannuation Service. Payroll is still decentralized, mostly at regional hospital board level, but the proposed reorganization could ultimately lead to a change in the location of this function too.

Partial service

There are many functions which can certainly not be undertaken entirely from the centre but for which some measure of central direction could be beneficial. The most obvious of these is supplies, for which the centre could:

a. Decide which items are to be provided through central contracts and which are to be purchased locally.

b. Place the contracts for the centrally supplied items.

c. Provide an advisory service to health boards on prices and standards for items to be purchased locally.

d. Set up procedures for health boards and other bodies to requisition supplies from central contracts and for efficient settlement of supplier's accounts.

There are in addition a number of subjects on which the Common Services Agency may be concerned primarily with the important function of the setting of standards, for instance for medical records, fire prevention, and catering. There are still others for which it could set standards as well as providing other aspects of the service. An example is personnel management where we consider it ought to assume over-all responsibility for manpower planning, to provide guidance on careers, recruitment, and promotions, and to delegate recruitment of some staff to health boards who may themselves delegate it still further. Payroll and superannuation procedures could be delegated to a data-processing facility, while advice on such diverse matters as pay and conditions of service and training could be best provided by a Common Services Agency of this kind.

3.3. Strategic objectives and corporate planning

Even after reorganization there will continue to be complex interrelationships between various bodies within the NHS, and between the NHS and other bodies, such as the Department of Education and Science, medical schools, the Medical Research Council (MRC), the various royal colleges, the DHSS, and local authorites. The new structure should, however, facilitate the recognition of major planning and operational levels, and the establishment of objectives which can be expressed in appropriate terms to each level of the NHS.

We have suggested in section 3.2 above that one of the main tasks of the central bodies should be in the realm of policy and planning which must be evolved in the general context of NHS objectives. In some cases objectives may be set for Scotland alone, in others the planning bodies may contribute to the setting of UK objectives, and in still others they may be concerned with interpretation of UK objectives in the light of conditions in Scotland.

To have the improved health of the population as a long-term objective is excellent, unexceptionable, and obvious. Both in the UK as a whole and in Scotland there is growing interest in achieving this concept as an alternative to merely attempting to provide a service geared to identified demand. It is already evident that there is a strong body of opinion in the NHS which recognizes the need to maximize the amount of health care within the constraints of available finance.

However, both improved health of the population and maximization of health care are of limited value to the GP or the hospital administrator because they are not expressed in terms of their day-to-day tasks. They are useful as statements of ends but at all levels of the NHS they must be developed into means which may be expressed in several ways. For instance:

a. In general terms such as the balance of effort and resources to be given to prevention, protection, or treatment on demand: the actual method will vary from one disease to another, and from one time to another.

b. In terms of a building or medical education programme required as a result of concentration on particular methods of treatment. This will involve wide-ranging policy co-ordination with other bodies such as the Department of Education and Science.

c. In terms of a research programme required if a change in the method of treatment is to be achieved. This will require co-ordination with the MRC.

d. In terms of a health education programme required to encourage the population to preserve its health.

The initial requirement is to bring these long-term needs together to form a strategic plan of development and to examine how they interact with one another. The function of the central authorities would be to interpret and define how and at what pace the over-all plan can be implemented. Further-more periodic reviews of the strategy would be required in the light of such matters as evolving social attitudes, government policy, and advances in medical science. The present tripartite structure does not readily lend itself to this approach but an integrated structure could benefit significantly from the adoption of an over-all planning approach based on the principles of corporate planning developed for industrial activities. Whilst a large part of the NHS's work will continue to be financed on a year-to-year budgeting basis it would be possible to give more attention to allocation of finance and deployment of existing resources to achieve the longer-term objectives. Already the building of new hospitals, the development of health centres and the development of computing facilities have been recognized as areas requiring a long-term strategy and financial policy to achieve maximum bene-fits. The principal factors which dictate this approach include:

a. The high total cost of developments.

b. The lengthy period required for developments.

c. The variable demand for finance.

d. The variable demand for staff of different skills.

e. The need to phase out present activities, redeploy staff, and reallocate spending.

We do not suggest that a single central planning organization would be able to perform this task unaided. Indeed it would rely heavily for professional guidance on specialist advisory groups for medical assessment of proposals and on an information service to provide and perhaps in many cases to inter-pret hard data relating to general proposals or specific situations.

3.4. Working objectives

After deliberations at the higher levels of the NHS it would be necessary to establish lower-level objectives of value to practitioners and administrators. If, for instance, in relation to a particular ailment a policy of protection by immunization had been decided upon it would be possible to establish a percentage of the population to be immunized in order to bring the ailment under satisfactory control.

In some cases the level and nature of care is the objective needing to be established. An outstanding example of this is maternity care, in which first a general statement on reduction in perinatal mortality and morbidity could be made, then the reduction might be quantified, and finally methods of achieving the reduction might be examined. The methods could be translated into a demand for buildings, beds, doctors, midwives, and all supporting services required, in the various areas of Scotland.

It will be necessary to examine the ways in which targets could be achieved. For immunization there are well-developed computer systems which can automatically schedule appointments and be fed with results from the clinic session; defaulters are readily identified and percentage achievements can easily be calculated. However, it is not so easy to decide how to increase an unsatisfactory percentage. For maternity requirements an increase in the building programme, requisitioning of buildings currently used for other purposes, and adjusting the priorities of other specialities are all possibilities which would need to be examined in the light of latest information and intelligence.

3.5. Monitoring and review

While development of an objective and its associated targets and methods of achievement will normally filter from the top level downwards through the system, review procedures may be initiated at any level, depending on the nature of the considerations which determined the original choice. Thus the development of a new vaccine can shift the major objective from prevention or screening to protection; the development of a cheap drug can change it from screening to treatment on demand. The availability of computers ought in itself to lead to new targets and achieved percentages in immunization programmes, and should enable many different kinds of follow-up programmes to be initiated. The very act of setting objectives may in some cases force attention on to the methods and resources required. The need for monitoring and review and the necessity on occasion to change objectives are acknowledged.

3.6. Conclusion

Much detailed development work is still required to establish the relationship of data, intelligence, planning, and assessment. This report is aimed specifically at data requirements and how data can be made available, as usable information, to the various planning and operational groups.

After the brief examination in this chapter therefore, the emergence of working relationships is assumed and the report will confine itself to major areas of data and the problems to be overcome if a viable data system is to be established. Not the least of these problems will be development of an information services' function, all but passing references to which have been avoided so far.

The avoidance was deliberate, as the information services are quite different from planning and operational services. They may need to use data, to evaluate it, and call for new forms of data, but in general the information services will supply data while planning and operational services will use it. The distinction needs to be recognized: the information services will ensure data is available at all levels, branches, and areas of the health services. In our opinion they cannot do this effectively unless they are a unified group, a concept which is discussed in more detail in Chapter 11. Chapter 11 also covers the future roles of SOCS and the Scottish Advisory Committee on Computers in the Health Service (SACCHS).

Examination of the role of one other body, the GRO, was specifically included in the terms of reference for this study. This is deferred to Chapter 5, where patient data is discussed, including the role of the NHSCR, which is at present maintained by the GRO.

4. Information requirements and the siting of databanks

4.1. The need for data

Some doctors and administrators believe that a data system implies an attempt to collect all data and to answer all questions from the resultant databank. At many interviews there was an unmistakable undercurrent of feeling that a major funds-consuming exercise might well be initiated in data collection, the cost of which would be out of all proportion to its effectiveness. This report, however, does not recommend collection of any data for which there is not a planned use.

There is also a belief that existence of a databank will result in all decisions being taken out of the hands of those who have to make the service work. Such beliefs are not restricted to people working in the NHS. They are commonly held by people who operate in an intuitive fashion, and believe that they do not need the assistance of data to make decisions at operational or planning levels. As an example, some people maintain that a group of 'experts' can be relied upon to solve a particular problem, for instance where to site a new laboratory or whether to provide expanded facilities at an existing one, and that data on current throughput and geographical distribution of the laboratory's samples is of comparatively little value. The experts know what is required, they know the workload because they have to handle it every day and they know where the samples came from.

This attitude does, however, presuppose a static pattern of activity which is uninfluenced by changes in resources, techniques, manpower, or costs. Most administrators and planners now recognize that accurate, up-to-date data must be the basis for both day-to-day decisions and forward planning and that there is an increasing need to examine in detail and over-all the cause and effect of variations in demand or growth. Casual extrapolations and 'rules of thumb' based on historical data may be useful checks but are of only limited value when compared with constant monitoring of activities coupled with the use of forecasting models.

Good data is not a substitute for professional judgement nor does the provision of data require withdrawal of responsibility for taking decisions. Data quantifies what has happened; decisions are the use of professional judgement to influence the future situation.

4.2. Concept of a databank

Theoretically a databank may be defined as the total amount of data in a system. Databanks are therefore no new idea. Each hospital, executive council, and local authority has its own databank; each department has its own databank; each doctor and each administrator even has his own databank. Each health board when established, will have its own databank, although the databank will be fragmented in many different locations and in incompatible forms unless positive action is taken to co-ordinate development. The amount of data in the NHS is vast and is constantly being added to and the problems of incompatibility and inaccessibility are already apparent. The perpetual addition of new data does not make it easier to withdraw the data required for a particular purpose. Much of it is initially transient, it is not captured as it arises and has to be recaptured, for instance by lengthy form-filling or file-searching operations, to be made useful.

4.3. Siting of databanks

It will be obvious from the functional levels described in the previous chapter that information required at different levels is different in type and will be put to quite different uses. The policymaker, the planner, the research worker, the line manager, and the staff officer, the doctor, the nurse, and the administrator have different outlooks and different needs although in many cases the data needs of one may be a summary, a rearrangement, an expansion, or an aggregation of the needs of another. For one purpose individually identified records may be essential, for another the same level of detail may be required but without identification, while for yet another purpose numerical summaries may be perfectly adequate.

The problem is to know what data is important, who is likely to need it and also to ensure it can be 'withdrawn' in the form required. The discussion of organization and objectives set out in the preceding chapter can now be turned to account. If the health board is to provide the broad range of health services within its own geographical boundaries, then it will need the data relating to its own geographical area in order to take decisions affecting the services provided. Similarly, the CSA which will be obliged to undertake a number of critical functions for the whole Scottish health service will require information on supplies, equipment, and suppliers, on manpower, buildings and their condition, and on any subject which the health service desires to monitor, including national morbidity statistics. Monitoring processes may be initiated by various groups within the CSA, the SHSPC, or the SHHD. The nature of the latter two bodies suggests that they will rely heavily on the CSA for information services rather than operate any form of databank themselves. Frequently, however, an interpretive function will be required which may take any of several forms, for instance statistical manipulation, correlation of hard data with soft intelligence, or subjective appreciation by multidisciplinary teams. These concepts are discussed in detail in Chapter 11.

4.4. The health board

Fig. 4.1 illustrates the flow of data from the periphery to health boards as a result of the organization which is to be established. The concentration of data at this level is very significant and is an inevitable consequence of the functions which the health board is to carry out.

There are a number of major activities for which data will be required as a basis for investigation and decision. These include:

a. Assessment of manpower requirements for the general medical, dental, ophthalmic, and pharmaceutical services, and any clerical support which these practitioners require.

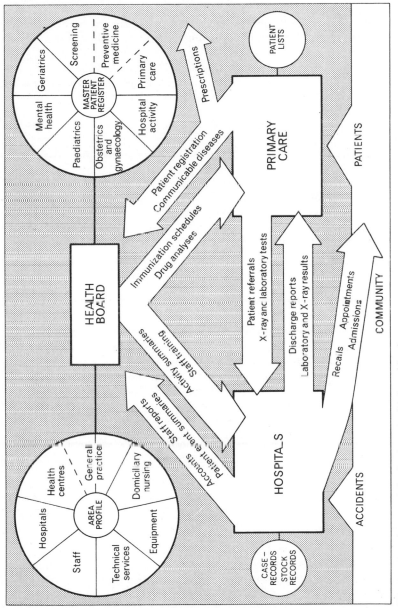

Fig. 4.1. Data flows and databanks at health board level

b. Assessment of potential workloads of the various hospital specialties and hence the number of staff of all kinds, premises, clinic sessions, and beds which are likely to be required in hospitals.

c. The engagement and assignment of staff for the purposes of immunization programmes, screening programmes, domiciliary visits, and the school health service.

d. Monitoring of the effectiveness of previous recommendations by examining, for example, trends in the size of waiting-lists, delays in completion of domiciliary visits or other scheduled activities, and delays in obtaining an out-patient appointment.

e. Provision of data to doctors, nurses, administrators, and other professional staff to enable them to conduct constructive inquiries into their own performance, particularly as compared with other staff in similar positions both in the same area and in other areas.

f. Provision of forecasts to enable staff to anticipate seasonal and other fluctuations in workload.

g. Assessment of policy decisions, for example, calculations of the potential effects of closing down a unit, or restricting admissions to emergencies only as opposed to endeavouring to maintain the unit with reduced availability of staff.

h. Optimizing the requirements of staff training, career development, and service to the community.

These services demand a knowledge of the population they are serving and of the resources which are immediately available.

The health board must therefore be able to identify:

a. The population within its area, classified according to age, sex, GP, residential locality, and occupation.

b. The 'health status' of specific groups of people, for example the stage a child has reached in an immunization programme, the next contact due for an infirm aged person or a person included in an established follow-up routine, and known allergies and susceptibilities.

c. The morbidity pattern of its area, and changes which are taking place in that pattern.

d. NHS manpower of all kinds available immediately, normally, and at peak holiday times or sickness periods. The mobility permissible.

e. Buildings and equipment available, their condition and running costs.

f. Supplies available and on order, their consumption rates, ages, and lead times on deliveries.

g. Transport available, its condition and running costs.

Attempts have been made to provide operational information from a national data-processing centre; an example is the development of hospital discharge form (SMR 1) processing by the Research and Intelligence Unit of the SHHD and SOCS (3). Although this is an excellent development, the necessity to collect huge quantities of data from a large number of widely dispersed locations, transfer it to a central point for processing and distribute the results caused unavoidable delays in the provision of operational data to the periphery, thus reducing substantially its value. The centre has recognized this fact and seems anxious to devolve initial processing to the local units, wherever it is possible to ensure maintenance of quality of the data.

The progress of SMR 1 with the centre taking the initiative, identifying problems and solving them, and then handing over operations to a local body, could well become a pattern for other developments. It is, however, a clear indication that the first level of data, and the decisions made on the basis of it, must always be placed at the point of origin. It is our recommendation therefore that each health board have its own databank, containing basic information about population and resources within its boundaries.

It must be noted that this recommendation cannot automatically be translated into a recommendation that each health board should from its inception have its own computer. At the time of the reorganization of the NHS the health boards will have to make use of existing facilities. After that date there should be a gradual extension of computer services within the framework of a national policy.

4.5. The central authorities

The central authorities (SHHD, SHSPC, and CSA) fulfil different functions from those of health boards. The flow of data to central authorities is shown in Fig. 4.2.

The essential difference is the longer-term nature of the work to be done. The central authorities should not be concerned so much with day-to-day management and control as with long-term investment decisions and with the probable effect of political decisions.

The decisions required at this level concern strategy, for instance:

a. Is the aim total or near-total elimination of certain diseases? If so, what does this imply in terms of screening, prophylaxis, or environmental improvements?

b. Is part of the diagnostic process to be placed on a routine basis, so that for instance a whole battery of tests is performed on each individual who comes into contact with the hospital?

c. Is a comprehensive laboratory, radiotherapy, ECG, or X-ray service to be provided in each health board?

d. Which areas are to provide services in the super-specialities?

e. On what criteria should the necessity for a new centre for a specialist service be based, and on what basis should its location be decided?

These are some of the broader issues with which the central bodies seem likely to be faced. To settle them they will need details of morbidity distributions and catchment areas of particular hospitals or laboratories. They will also need to take into account the manpower implications of each individual proposal and of any building work necessary, and a databank of summarized patient, personnel, and building information will be required. At this level in particular, hard data must be complemented by intelligence and interpretation, since the opportunity to take a completely objective 'absolute' viewpoint will occur comparatively rarely. Usually ideal solutions will have to be tempered by the exigencies of existing situations.

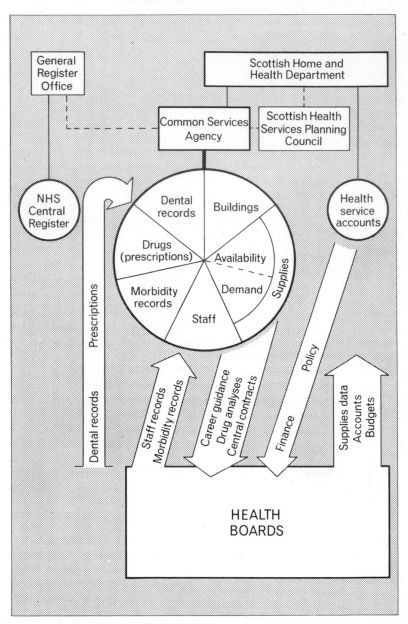

Fig. 4.2. Data flows and databanks at central level

Data will be required centrally for other purposes also, such as:

a. Research, especially epidemiological research, and assistance to research workers.

b. Manpower planning, including assistance in formulating policies on recruitment, promotion, and retirement.

c. Remuneration, including advice to SHHD on pay negotiations.

d. Prescription pricing and dental estimates work, including the compilation of management analyses. This work could well follow the development pattern of hospital discharge form processing, being undertaken centrally at first and subsequently being devolved to the regions.

e. Operations research, including simulations and model-building.

The databanks held centrally should therefore include data on:

a. Each major significant episode of morbidity. The term 'major significant episode' currently has no precise definition but could initially mean all episodes which include one or more spells of in-patient treatment or investigation. It has long been recognized, however, that in-patient statistics provide an imperfect guide to morbidity and the means of making an early extension of data collection to ambulatory care should be sought. Birth and death should also be classified as major episodes.

b. Prices, dosages, and suppliers of drugs, and indexes of prescriptions, by doctor, patient, and chemist.

c. Costing of dental treatment, past records of patients, and indexes of treatment, by dentist and patient.

d. Items and suppliers of supplies and equipment, including stocks, prices, delivery periods, usage, and economic order quantities.

e. Grades, salaries, and previous postings, for all employed and contracted staff. Annual progress reports on professional, technical, administrative, clerical, and nursing staff.

Much of this data could be drawn from databanks operated by health boards (for instance, all 'medical' data, and a substantial amount of the manpower data) and some will be provided as a by-product of existing operational procedures (for instance, most drugs and dental data, stocks); other data may be acquired as a result of new procedures (suppliers, the rest of the manpower data, drug dosages), but even this would be data which already exists in the NHS.

It is as important here as in the previous section to recognize that the necessity for central databanks does not imply the installation of computers immediately following reorganization of the NHS.

It will however almost certainly be found desirable for individual functions to have ready access to a small versatile machine: particular examples are manpower planning and operations research, which will often need to extract the data they require from large files before processing it frequently and rapidly.

4.6. Summary

Data is not a substitute for professional judgement, but the foundation on which good judgement stands. No data should be collected unless it has a known use.

The health board is to provide the health services to the public and must therefore have the data on which to base its short-term and day-to-day management. The central authorities will need extracts of the data held by health boards for strategic planning but in some cases will provide a total service for reasons of economy and ease of management.

Databanks do not necessarily require computers but for high volume activities computer facilities should be installed and extended gradually.

5. People and patients

The Scottish health service has over 5 million potential customers. In the course of a year these customers account for 650,000 hospital admissions, 8 million attendances at out-patient departments, 28 million prescriptions, 2 million courses of dental treatment, 600,000 eye-tests, 90,000 births and 60,000 deaths, and hundreds of thousands of immunizations, laboratory tests, X-rays, and other investigations.

The facilities for treatment are provided by three separate administrative branches of the health service, consequently a large number of authorities compile and retain data about patients. Some authorities, for example the GRO and executive councils, also compile and retain data about people for health service purposes, whether they are patients or not.

The unified administration of the future will make any arrangements considered necessary for the provision of hospital and general medical services, employing health visitors, organizing school clinics, and operating immunization programmes. It will, therefore, need data on people including potential and past patients, not just existing patients. The roles of health boards and central authorities have been explored in Chapters 3 and 4 and some reference was made to the kind of data required at different administrative levels of the health services. We now turn to the detailed requirements for patient data.

5.1. Computerized patient records
It is permissible to speculate briefly on the prospect of all data on every patient being collected and stored in a nationwide computer facility. Planning such a system would take many years, the plans being subject to change by successive health service administrations and regularly being overtaken by technology and innovation. The prospect may eventually be realized but it is one to which no more than passing reference can be made when considering developments in the immediate future. Such a comprehensive system would be difficult to establish, enormously costly, and of doubtful practical value. The discussion which follows considers data now available and ways in which it may be augmented and used.

5.2. Data now available
There are two principal existing collections of patient data. First there are a number of registers and secondly there are details amassed from hospital discharge forms (SMR 1). The registers are headed by the NHSCR, in which there is at least one entry for virtually every member of the community. Other registers are related to particular subjects or groups such as cancer, blind, handicapped, 'at risk', thyroid, immunization, and cervical cytology screening. For the most part these registers consist of little more than identification data and are used as a reference source or occasionally for scheduling of a future consultation. They contain a small amount of information about

a large number of people and much of the information is duplicated between one register and another. Hospital discharge forms are now collected for all in-patients from general, mental health, and maternity hospitals. They contain more information about a smaller number of people but even so much of the information is for identification purposes and duplicates that held on the various registers.

5.3. The master register: an opportunity

The establishment of health boards, responsible for all aspects of medical care, provides an excellent opportunity to rationalize the entire system of registers and records.

The primary requirement is to establish a basic or master register, such as the one depicted in Fig. 5.1, of the population in an area and to provide a means of referencing or linking all other sets of data to it. The basic record for each person would be similar to that currently held by executive councils.

Existing executive council records have many omissions and inaccuracies, especially concerning addresses but also extending to fundamental data such as date of birth and NHS number. The files are also inflated by records of people who are no longer resident in the area (the level of inflation varies from one executive council to another and in one case is as high as 11 per cent).

These shortcomings must largely be attributed to the limited use made of the records and would need to be removed from any system of health board master registers. As part of the process of establishing the master register records would have to be vetted for accuracy, omissions, and non-residents to bring them to an acceptable state. Absolute perfection is not essential and would be unlikely ever to be achieved, but if the records were thereafter used for an ever-increasing number of purposes the incentive and the means for improving accuracy would be available.

The users of such a register could increase rapidly if information on special situations, currently held in numerous other registers, were added. Such data could range from immunization status, through special risk situations such as the thyroid and cervical cytology follow-up programmes to research registers such as the cancer register.

Establishment of this register is vital to both initial and continued planning of health board work. If used in conjunction with the annual population estimates prepared by the GRO, it would provide the base from which to assess the needs of the area for various services. For instance, an analysis of the age distribution would provide some guidance on the relative demands to be expected for paediatric, maternity, and geriatric care. Cross-tabulation for independent assessments could also be readily made, for instance, of the number of blind, handicapped, and diabetics in the community.

Doctors, planners, and managers alike must be able to rely on a source of accurate information which in turn would provide the incentive to proper maintenance.

The basic register would thus become the focal point in organizational and operational activity rather than a mere reference source for payment of GPs. There would be no need to maintain separate national registers for special groups such as the blind and cancer patients as any central requirements for data on these categories could be drawn from health board sources as the

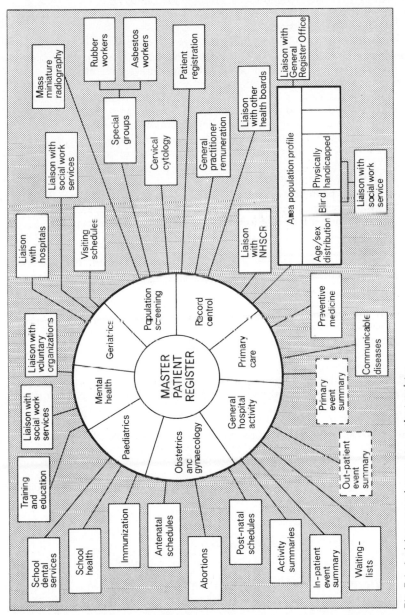

Fig. 5.1. Activity centred on master patient register

need arose. There would, however, be a continuing need to maintain a single national index (NHSCR) and this is discussed in section 5.8.

5.4. Hospital discharge data

The basic register would be part of a hierarchical system. An immediately available and important source of data is to be found in hospital in-patient discharge forms. If these are to be regarded as a vital source of data on hospital operational activity and not merely as a source of morbidity statistics, analyses will have to be done at regular intervals and the results disseminated quickly to individual hospitals and consultants. Where practical, individual hospitals could process the data themselves.

There is an increasing need to collect similar data for out-patients and this must be initiated once the integrated health service is under way.

5.5. Routine data requirements

It has not been possible in a study of this kind to identify precisely the data which will be required for each individual activity but there is little doubt that the following will be required for one purpose or another:

5.5.1. *Identification*

It is essential to be able to identify the patient with certainty. This will consist of at least surname, first names, sex, date of birth, and birth surname.

5.5.2. *Reference*

At birth, or on initial registration for immigrants, each person is allocated an NHS number. It is unique to each person and could become an invaluable reference number (this is discussed in Chapter 13).

5.5.3. *Location*

Full postal address, telephone number, and postcode. Temporary addresses, such as the hospital or home of long-stay patients, should also be included.

5.5.4. *Civil status*

Married, single, widowed, etc., the number of children and perhaps also their NHS numbers, next of kin, guardian or responsible person.

5.5.5. *Occupation*

A broad classification but with some special categories recognized, such as asbestos and rubber workers.

5.5.6. *Assignment*

The GP with whom the person is registered.

5.5.7. *Education*

(Persons under 18.) The school being attended.

5.5.8. *General health*

a. Immunization status.

b. Blood group.

c. Allergies.

d. Allocation to special risk categories.

5.5.9. *Current health*

a. Current waiting-list details.

b. Current in-patient details.

c. Current major therapy.

5.5.10. *Health history*

a. Major diagnoses and operations.

b. Hospital case-notes indexes.

c. Previous health boards.

The above list may appear to contain vast amounts of data, yet all this data is already held within the NHS, indeed much of it is repeated in many different incompatible and sometimes inaccessible files. Our recommendations are designed to reduce the total quantity of data, by removing repetition of the same items, and at the same time to make data more accessible by having a single reference point.

It should not be imagined that we propose the immediate establishment of registers containing the entire range of data listed. Development of the databank will require careful planning and dedicated work over a number of years and a suggested approach is set out in section 12.3.

5.6. Use by health boards and lower levels

We have set out the data as though it were a single 'personal' record for each member of the community but it is not sufficient to consider it merely in this light. The data has to be capable of manipulation, that is to say various selections from it must be made available to various people at various times.

For instance, those responsible for providing the school health services have to know all children of specific ages and the schools they attend in order to schedule the duties of school doctors. They may not require other data however.

Similarly each speciality will need to analyse its own workload at regular intervals but may have no requirement for other data. Each will also have to provide the data which enables such sections as 'waiting-list' to be established. This kind of data can best be supplied as a result of decisions to admit a person to the waiting-list and to select a person from the waiting-list. Full control of decisions of this nature is vested in the doctor concerned, but the holding of numerous waiting-lists is an administrative function which in our opinion can most effectively be undertaken by health boards. From waiting-lists, health boards can assess trends and changing demands in all specialties throughout the area.

Both the examples given, namely children of specific ages and waiting-list data, could be dealt with by computer file inversion techniques from a single total record. It would also be necessary to select sections of the total file for a variety of purposes such as provision of profiles of health for a particular hospital or health centre, or even for an individual doctor. A promising open-ended subfile system has been discussed by the subcommittee on organization and interchange of data set up by the SACCHS.

5.7. Use by central bodies

All the examples so far are related to use either at health board level or below. Patient data also has considerable value on a national scale and the central bodies will need to draw upon it in order to pursue research work or to assist with major problems.

The Research and Intelligence Unit of the SHHD in collaboration with the SOCS has overcome many difficulties during the past few years to bring the processing of discharge summaries to an acceptable standard. The principle of devolution to the regions has been accepted, with the proviso that all the data must still be made available, perhaps in tape or card form, to the Research and Intelligence Unit.

Elimination of special punching procedures will have to be tackled if the logical extensions to out-patient departments and health centres are to be attempted.

We believe the siting of the patient databank at health board level will enable faster turnround of data to the user to be made, and will increase speed and accuracy of data-processing at the centre.

5.8. Position of the National Health Service Central Register

The NHSCR is now maintained by the GRO acting as an agent of the SHHD. It consists of seven different registers, each of which has an NHS number of distinctive format, and each held in NHS number sequence. A nominal index is maintained to the registers, in which are recorded names, dates of birth, and original addresses, together with details of each executive council within whose area the person has been registered. The register is useful as a focal point for contacts with England and Wales and the Armed Forces. It also provides a measure of confidentiality for persons who are re-registered following adoption or imprisonment, in that it is not possible for the executive council or other local body to discover the historical record. The NHSCR is also being found increasingly useful by medical research workers, often in conjunction with the English NHSCR at Southport.

There are suggestions that the NHSCR should no longer be maintained by the GRO, especially if a CSA were to be set up as part of a unified health service. The recording of a greater amount of detail in the NHSCR has also been suggested, for instance inclusion of the name of the doctor with whom a person is registered rather than just the executive council.

We do not agree with either of these suggestions for the following reasons:

a. To transfer maintenance of the NHSCR to the NHS itself seems logical enough. However, much more communication would be required between the GRO and the NHS for notification of vital events and it would be more difficult to maintain the confidentiality of the register were it to be placed within the boundaries of the NHS and therefore in direct contact with health boards.

b. The recording of more detail is said to be required because the NHSCR is one of the few regular sources of migration statistics. The geographical area covered by some executive councils is too large to provide the detailed analysis required, a drawback which will be magnified when there are fourteen health boards instead of twenty-five executive councils. To increase the amount of detail recorded in a vast central register for the purpose of supplying migration *statistics* is extremely inefficient, particularly when the health board has to keep itself informed of its population, and should be able to supply migration statistics in suitable form. Only if the NHSCR is to replace all executive council lists would the recording of more detail be justified. We believe the NHSCR's relationship to executive councils and future health boards should continue to be that of a focal point and general index.

5.9. Summary

Existing registers and discharge data can be developed into a unified system, providing useful information to all levels of the service. The information must be usable for forward operational scheduling as well as for retrospective analyses and future longer-term planning.

We believe that the GRO should continue to maintain the NHSCR.

6. Personnel

The largest single item of revenue expenditure in the NHS is on staff. It accounts for over 60 per cent of the total annual costs incurred in providing the wide-ranging facilities available to the general public. It is a significant item in each of the main branches of the NHS.

Several important studies relating to staffing in the NHS have been undertaken in recent years covering subjects such as training (4), staff structure (5,6,7), and workload assessment (8,9). There has been a need to collect, process, and assess data on different groups of staff as part of these studies and in some of these reports (5,6) recommendations have been made which recognize the need for a continuous process of data capture and assessment.

We have assumed that the Scottish health service in common with many other organizations wishes to operate a broad policy of conserving trained manpower by providing rewarding employment and career prospects for the individuals employed in the service.

However, the present arrangements for handling manpower activities in the NHS are, in general, too fragmented to provide the basis for an effective system. For example there are no formal links between the Scottish Hospital Administrative Staffs Committee (SHASC), Scottish Nursing Staffs Committee (SNSC), the Scottish Home and Health Department's (SHHD) manpower planning unit, the various Whitley Councils, and medical staff appointment committees. The exchange of information and co-ordination of policy on activities such as manpower planning, recruitment, promotion, career guidance, staff training, and other personnel activities falls far short of our assessment of health service requirements.

6.1. A personnel information system

Personnel management and manpower planning are dynamic activities: they deal with situations which can change for a variety of reasons, some controllable, some uncontrollable. An essential feature in these activities is, therefore, a steady inflow of up-to-date information on individual members of staff together with a corresponding return flow of analyses and assessments. This process requires:

a. Close co-ordination and communication between policymaking, planning, and personnel management.

b. A satisfactory source of basic data on the individual members of staff employed in the organization.

c. An effective means for processing the data and presenting it to those responsible for planning, recruitment, promotion, career development, and other functions.

If maximum benefit is to be derived from an improved system it is essential that a single source of basic data is established which contains an indivi-

Table 6.1. *Major items of data for personnel management*

Item	Examples of data
Surname	
First names	
Date of birth	
Category	(Medical, nursing, administrative)
Grade	(Consultant, CNO)
Salary basis	(Hourly, monthly, contractor)
Salary	
Employment authority	
Date of appointment	
Previous employment	(Post, employer)
Method of appointment	(Recruited, promoted, transferred)
Nature of appointment	(Full-time, part-time, seconded)
Date of leaving	
Reasons for leaving	(Retired, resigned, transferred)
Subsequent employment	(Post, employer)
Place of work	Health board
	Unit
Qualifications	(MB, Ch B, MA, SRN, FCA)

dual record for all professional career-grade staff employed by, or contracted to, the NHS. Such a databank would, however, be subject to the usual strict security controls and confidentiality accorded to personnel data.

Current attempts to develop the use of superannuation and payroll data for manpower planning activities are praiseworthy but are unlikely to prove satisfactory since neither is comprehensive in coverage; that is not *all* staff are on the payroll or are superannuable.

Much of the basic personal data used for payroll is very specialized and hardly relevant to the more general personnel management activities and vice versa. Payroll and personnel data could not be checked against one another for accuracy and validity and it would be necessary to have independent up-dating arrangements. The different procedures currently in operation for dealing with remuneration would require extensive rationalization before a central payroll activity could be set up. For example, there are particular criteria to be met for staff on weekly pay; different procedures are used for hospital doctors, GPs, and dentists. Whilst it would be advantageous to the NHS to carry out a reappraisal of these procedures as part of the longer-term activities a central databank for personnel management purposes is a more urgent requirement. At this stage there seems little point in attempting to combine payroll and personnel data in a single record and we have therefore indicated in Table 6.1 the main items of information which should be included in a personnel databank; we consider that this simple form of record would meet immediate needs but additional or alternative items might be required when the personnel systems become more highly developed. These records would be a contracted form of the full personnel record which would be held at unit or health board level.

A set of such records held and maintained centrally would be an adequate base for servicing the various short-term needs for manpower and staff information. The collection and maintenance of general personnel information is of such importance that a positive short-term programme to establish a system would be beneficial. This need not preclude the longer-term development of payroll-personnel linkage which is discussed in Chapter 12.

The present fragmented arrangements for staff recruiting, promotion, and general personnel servicing compared with normal industrial practice suggests that a review of manpower management methods in the NHS is long overdue. We have observed a lack of commitment to maintain staff data at supervisory level and in particular many people do not appreciate the importance of communicating such data to higher levels in the organization. An important objective of a review should be to establish a personnel information system with a central personnel databank; this could act as a focal point and channel for communication between the various activities which provide the basis for control and deployment of manpower, such as pay and conditions of service, recruitment, appointment and promotion, payroll and superannuation, and manpower planning.

We therefore recommend that a central personnel databank be set up in order to provide an up-to-date and complete quantitative view of the manpower situation in the NHS. The main benefits which we consider would be derived from such a databank are as follows:

a. The early identification of any change in staff trends.

b. The availability of accurate data on which to base national and local recruiting policy.

c. The availability of accurate data on which to base promotion and appointment decisions.

d. The provision of data for manpower planning studies.

e. The analysis of data to assist with pay negotiations.

We believe that there is already a need in the NHS for a broad-ranging activity on manpower planning which will involve all levels of the service from individuals to central policy planning. It is important therefore to ensure that adequate attention is given to the gathering and assessment of data upon which specific and adaptive policy can be based for activities such as recruitment, deployment, career development, and training.

An important underlying implication is the ability to make an assessment (and undertake periodic reassessment) of current and forward manpower needs to meet the expected workload in terms of both staff groups and grades and in area and unit deployment. Good data will also facilitate the simulation of the effects of policy decisions upon the manpower structure.

6.2. Short-term development programme

If these objectives are to be met it will be necessary to process and present the data to the various functional groups at regular intervals. In addition, analyses of groups or subgroups of staff records for the various staff committees concerned with appointment and promotions must be produced on demand. In the short term the analyses should be limited to 'current assessment' supported by recent historical data on turnover for broad groups of staff such as: hospital medical staff, GPs, hospital nurses, domiciliary nurses, etc.

The basic assessment would include: total size of group, breakdown by age, breakdown by deployment (initially by health board), breakdown by age within deployment group.

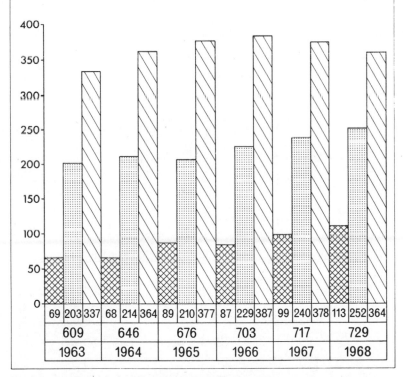

Category		Grade
A	▨	upper
B	▨	middle
C	▨	lower

69	203	337	68	214	364	89	210	377	87	229	387	99	240	378	113	252	364
609			646			676			703			717			729		
1963			1964			1965			1966			1967			1968		

Fig. 6.1. Comparison of staff complement over six years

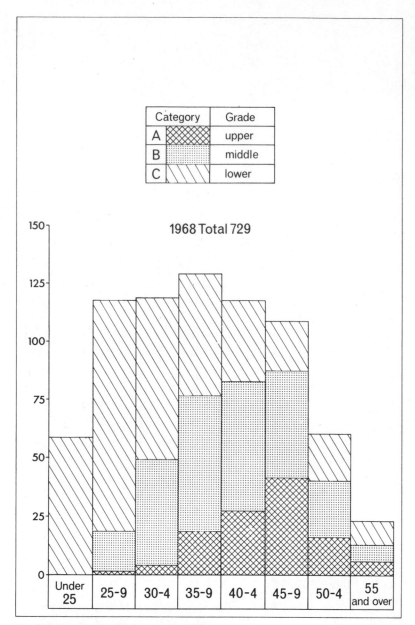

Category		Grade
A		upper
B		middle
C		lower

1968 Total 729

Fig. 6.2. Age-distribution of staff in 1968

These assessments should also be supported by turnover data (subdivided into losses and gains) as follows:

Gains. Recruitment, transfer-in, promotion-in.

Losses. Retirement, transfer-out, promotion-out, other wastage.

It would also be beneficial to consider the presentation of turnover data in these breakdowns as a second stage of the short-term programme.

An example of data analysed and presented in this way is given in Figs. 6.1-6.4, which represent the staff of one division of a large commercial organization. Whilst these are fairly basic presentations of staff data they are collectively of considerable value for both general and particular assessments of the staffing situation. Data is available in the NHS on total staff complements (Fig. 6.1) for the majority of staff groups. Age-distribution data (Fig. 6.2) is also available for hospital medical staff but it seems doubtful whether this data is readily available for other staff groups. Data does not seem to be currently available in the NHS to prepare Figs. 6.3 and 6.4.

In our view the SHHD Manpower Planning Unit should undertake the short-term programme as the initial stage of a more comprehensive manpower planning activity. We assume that continuity of work would be assured after the reorganization by incorporating manpower planning into a broader personnel organization such as that indicated in Fig. 6.5.

6.3. Long-term aims

Following on from this short-term development there could be established a comprehensive system covering historical review, current assessment, and forward estimating of manpower requirements, which is both qualitative and quantitative in nature.

Broadly based adaptive forecasting techniques are being increasingly used in large organizations as an aid to formulating and testing general planning policy. These techniques also provide valuable guidance for formulating overall and local policy on recruitment and promotion of staff. A simple forecast summary is illustrated in Table 6.2. A substantial amount of experience has already been gained in the use of these techniques by organizations such as the British Petroleum Co. Ltd, and we recommend that the NHS should endeavour to draw on this experience and examine in detail the application of the relevant computer programs for health service manpower planning work. work.

6.4. Organization

Much of the detailed reorganization of the NHS structure has still to be crystallized and we can therefore present only an outline scheme for a personnel information system. The main requirements are outlined below:

6.4.1. *Unit and health board level*

Individual detailed records for personnel employed will cover two major categories of staff, namely professional and career grades, and service and support staff.

The activities which will be carried out either at unit or at health board level will vary according to category and grade of staff but will include the following: Recording of duty (time-keeping); scheduling of duty; scheduling

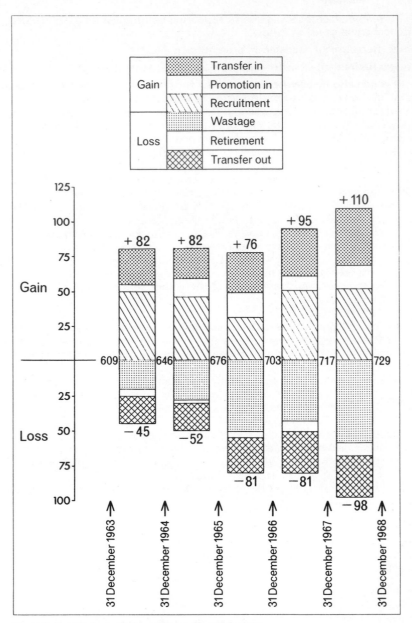

Fig. 6.3. Comparison of changes in staff complement

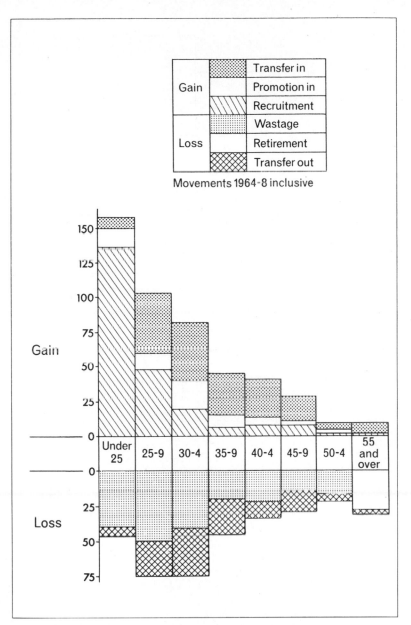

Fig. 6.4. Cumulative changes in staff complement over five years by age

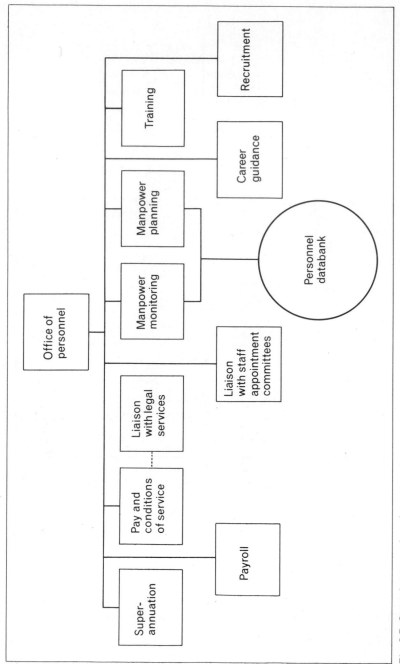

Fig. 6.5. Central personnel services

Table 6.2. *Summary of a simple forecast*

| | Manpower age-brackets | | | | | | | | |
	20-4	25-9	30-4	35-9	40-4	45-9	50-4	55-9	Total
Present strength	12	31	28	55	33	29	19	23	230
Average retention rate (percentage)	92	94	95·5	97·5	99	99	97·5	87·5	
Retention of present employees after five years	8	23	23	50	31	27	14		176
Corrected age-brackets for retained employees		8	23	23	50	31	27	14	176
Anticipated Intake during next five years	21	30	9						60
Number remaining in this	11	24	16	3					54
Forecast strength in five years	11	32	39	26	50	31	27	14	230
Net change after five years	−1	+1	+1	−29	+17	+2	+8	−9	0

of leave; recruitment; promotion and appointment (of senior grades); career guidance, development, training, and postgraduate education; remuneration (senior and contracted staff) and payroll; manpower reviews.

6.4.2. *Central activities*

The central personnel functions should be brought together on a more formal basis than hitherto, so as to make the best use of the manpower available to the NHS whilst providing the most rewarding career opportunities to individuals.

We have indicated a possible organization of the central personnel activities in Fig. 6.5. In particular we have indicated the need for unification and control under an office of health service personnel and there are two principal reasons for this:

a. There is a need for clear policy in personnel activities.

b. If a central personnel databank is to be set up it must be specifically under the control of a senior administrator.

We recommend this arrangement as a suitable basis for effectively organizing the following activities: Negotiation of pay and conditions of service; superannuation; recruitment policy; career guidance, development, and training policy; manpower monitoring; manpower planning.

6.5. Maintenance of the data base

The value of a personnel information system and in particular a staff record databank will be significantly influenced by the procedures adopted for maintaining and updating the records. We draw attention to Chapter 16 on data capture and in particular stress the need in this case to operate suitable procedures for maintaining the records. We believe that responsibility for notifying changes to existing staff records and the onward transmission of records for new staff must be firmly placed on supervising staff at working level. This will require positive action from the centre and in particular it will be necessary to convince supervisory staff of the all-round benefits which will accrue. Supervisory staff should be committed to maintaining up-to-date staff records and to communicating such data onwards through the system as part of their regular duties.

It seems probable that the procedures now being set up by the SHASC and the SNSC would be suitable for this purpose for administrative and nursing staff respectively. But similar bodies would be required to deal with other career and professional staff such as doctors, pharmacists, engineers, and architects.

We recommend that this matter be given early attention in the context of a health service personnel information system. In particular, we consider it would be of significant benefit in the process of integration and redeployment of staff if the terms of reference of the SHASC were extended immediately to embrace all administrative staff including those employed by executive councils, the Drug Pricing Bureaux, and the Dental Estimates Board and similarly for the SNSC to embrace domiciliary nurses now employed in the local authority health service.

6.6. Summary

Manpower is the biggest single resource in the NHS; the expenditure on manpower management and control should more closely reflect the importance of this activity and we therefore recommend that early consideration be given to reviewing and strengthening the effort devoted to this area. The various central personnel activities should be reorganized to provide the best service possible to the health boards. A central databank of staff data should be set up as a matter of some urgency to serve personnel planning activities.

7. Supplies

Organizations faced with increasing costs of supplies can take a number of courses of action. They can:

1. Reduce quantities used by imposing strict controls.
2. Buy cheaper alternatives (usually lower quality).
3. Rationalize the range of goods and the procedures for procurement.

The first two are frequently resorted to but can seldom be more than short-term solutions and have the very obvious drawback of restricting the service provided. Moreover, in any organization which is technically or scientifically orientated these procedures can be applied only to supporting items, such as foodstuffs, typewriter ribbons, and paper-clips which have a limited effect on total costs. The possibilities of economy by reductions in either consumption or price must always be examined, and certainly efforts to reduce waste and avoid needless 'quality' need to be maintained.

However, to achieve any long-term continuing benefit it is necessary to keep under constant review the range of items purchased and the procedures for procurement. Reviews of the range of items are as appropriate to technical and scientific supplies as to supporting items and an improved procurement procedure is as useful for the one as for the other. Each range of items needs to be viewed critically in the light of the service it is intended to provide.

7.1. The present position

The hospital supplies organization has been under scrutiny by a specially established committee since 1965. A report (10) has recently been prepared indicating that a reorganization of the supplies function and a rationalization of procurement policy are required. The report indicates that past purchasing policy has had three main drawbacks:

a. The various local and regional organizations have operated on an *ad-hoc* basis

b. Where central contracts have been arranged there has been no obligation at local level to requisition goods from these contracts.

c. Very little attention has been given to setting standards, consequently there have been wide variations in value for money and many instances of small quantities of a number of very similar items being used.

These matters are dealt with at some length in the report and we are broadly in agreement with the views expressed on rationalization of procurement policy.

Further evidence of the attention being given to supplies is provided by the important groundwork already done by the various specification working groups set up jointly by the SHHD and the DHSS.

The scope of these activities should however be progressively extended until it covers the complete range of supplies used in the NHS. Initially the aim should be to establish outline requirements with points of detail being agreed as part of the continuing process of revision. These standards should not therefore be regarded as fixed and inflexible; they will need revision from time to time to meet charges in NHS needs, to take advantage of experience gained at unit level and to make full use of available products.

7.2. The use of a data system

The report on hospital supplies outlined a number of arguments which had been put forward against central contracts. They are for the most part well refuted in the report itself and the difficulties described really amount to criticism of a badly managed system. There are large organizations in the distributive trade which do not experience those difficulties to anything like the same extent, yet they are broadly comparable to the NHS in that they have a large number of widely dispersed user points each taking up only part of a total order. The rate at which local units take up goods from large contracts, that is the call-off rate, is rarely uniform and one objective of a data system should be to establish what the variations are likely to be. Consumption may be confined to a particular group of user points (for instance, some supplies used in maternity hospitals will not be used in mental hospitals or health centres), will not be uniform between user points because of variations in size, nor in many cases will consumption be uniform throughout the year. Furthermore total consumption and patterns of consumption may change from year to year and an effective supplies system will require:

a. That adequate up-to-date data is available at all levels in the organization.

b. That there is regular direct contact between users, health boards, and the central procurement agency.

The over-all aim should be to establish a system of control which is sensitive and responsive to user needs but which also ensures that the cost of purchasing supplies is kept as low as possible. This does not imply total central contracting but it does require that data is readily available to assess whether centralized or decentralized purchasing arrangements will be more economic in a constantly changing supply and demand situation.

The supplies used in the NHS naturally cover a very wide range from high-cost items such as X-ray equipment through to bulk goods like bandages and butter. Attention will have to be given to establishing categories of supplies which need to be selected and handled on different criteria. The main categories appear to be:

a. Durable goods and equipment, which break into two sub-categories:

(i) Items requiring a continuing supply of parts or servicing (e.g. typewriters, X-ray equipment).

(ii) General items (e.g. furniture, bed linen, crockery).

b. Consumable goods which may be seasonal or in continuous demand; these also break into two sub-categories:

(i) Items directly associated with equipment or other durable goods (e.g. X-ray film, filters, typewriter ribbon).

(ii) General items (e.g. butter, paint, stationery, fuel).

c. General medical goods including sterile supplies, sterilizing chemicals, and so on.

General medical goods could be regarded as a sub-category of consumable goods but it may be that the criteria for selection are sufficiently important to make a distinction from general goods. However, the formulation of categories needs more detailed study and it might be considered more useful to have main categories covering patient care, administration, and patient accommodation for future costing exercises.

Across these categories there are also special features in subgroups of supplies which have a bearing on call-off rate, handling, or storage. For instance, some supplies are perishable, some require refrigerated storage, and some are toxic, radioactive, light sensitive, or sterile.

There is no reason for 'personal preference' to influence selection except within the bounds of established standards. This does not imply the introduction of an inflexible drab uniformity but restriction of choice to those items where it is really important. For example, choice of colour or pattern may be important for furnishing materials but personal preference for particular branded foodstuffs is not compatible with efficient procurement, nor can one be sure that the same preference would in fact be voiced by the majority of the consumers.

More attention is now being given to procedures which will overcome previous shortcomings but a concerted effort will be needed to maximize the considerable purchasing power of the NHS. The needs for data collection and handling must be viewed in the light of both short- and long-term activity which we suggest should be as follows.

7.3. Short-term activity

The short-term aim should be to collect and study information which can be used to establish a new procurement policy when the health boards and CSA are set up. The basic need is to capture data at user points (hospitals, health centres, and administrative offices) on quality, quantity, and price. This data should be aggregated to establish total demands in quality categories and actual costs. Work on stores accounting already carried out by regional hospital boards on behalf of boards of management should provide a useful starting-point.

The independence of each hospital group and the provision of stores accounting as a service may have resulted in many incompatible methods of recording, and one of the first needs will be to reconcile these. This reconciliation may also uncover a method of recording and handling data which can be applied throughout the service. Rationalized ranges should be established for each main line of goods and in the first instance outline standards of quality should be established. It will then be necessary to estimate the spread of total demand across the new range to produce breakdowns for contracting.

In parallel with this aggregation of local demand, data must be collected centrally on corresponding quality, prices, and delivery for bulk orders. The local and central collections of data taken together will provide a sound basis on which to establish a more effective procurement policy. In Fig. 7.1 we have illustrated a central contracts group which embraces the two databanks discussed above. This is a modified form of the organizational structure given in Appendix VII of the report on hospital supplies.

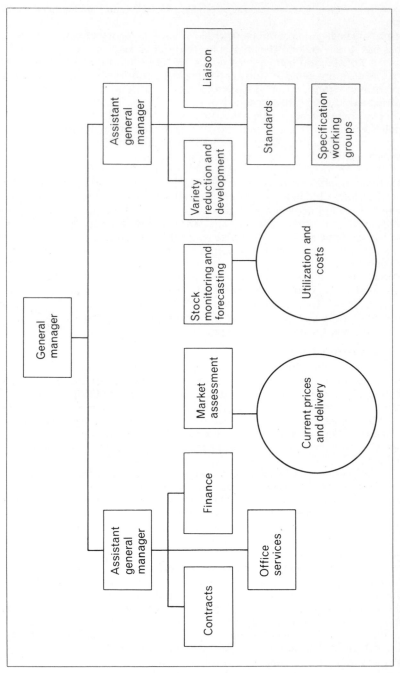

Fig. 7.1. Central supplies organization

7.4. Long-term activity

The long term must be concerned with the continuing development of techniques. Once sufficient data on consumption has been accumulated, forecasting techniques can be added to 'stock-on-hand' and 'stock-on-order' data when deciding how much to order. It is unlikely that less than two years' accumulated data will be sufficient as a basis for forecasting, hence the need to make use of any current data from stores accounting procedures to build up the data base as soon as possible.

In commercial environments it is usual to establish a service policy expressed as the target percentage of orders to be met from stock. (In some aspects of NHS work, this practice will be considered unacceptable, but to guarantee always to meet a demand for any particular item requires infinite stock. There will always be a chance, however slight, that an activity has to be postponed because some essential item is missing.) When determining stock policy, management has to determine first what probability of a 'stock-out' is acceptable, and secondly what delay in satisfying demand can be tolerated. The second aspect, tolerable delay, is all-important as it will determine the practicality of establishing common intermediate storage points which in turn will affect the acceptable 'stock-out' percentage.

NHS management needs to be able to experiment with different service levels and different distribution networks. In certain cases the real-life situation is too critical to allow any but the most circumspect experimentation and the ability to simulate the effects of various policies would be extremely useful. After the development of forecasting and the introduction of the concept of basic service policy we suggest that the technique of simulation might be a logical next development.

7.5. Conclusion

The control of supplies is, like personnel management, a dynamic activity. Demand, prices, and the range of goods available change, often quite quickly, and the system of control must be sensitive and responsive to such change if costs are to be minimized. This process periodically involves major reviews which may impinge on other activities. The effective review of methods and the development of efficient policy have been inhibited in the past owing to fragmentation of responsibility and a lack of up-to-date information. The strong central supplies organization recommended in the recent report (10) will be able to undertake major reviews on procurement and provide effective support for routine supplies activities, if it is provided with the right data and can develop a useful array of techniques.

8. Drugs

The annual cost of drugs is increasing and accounts for some 12-14 per cent of NHS expenditure in Scotland. The cost of drugs prescribed by GPs is approaching £20 million and hospital prescribing costs account for a further £6 million annually. The possibility of abuse, the short life of many drugs, and the spiralling costs therefore demand a greater degree of control than was desirable or practicable in the past and this in turn necessitates a satisfactory flow of information for both medical and managerial purposes.

8.1. Clinical and research requirements

The general information available to a doctor, or the service as a whole on the relative merits of different classes, brands, and strengths of drugs is poorly presented. A considerable improvement could be achieved by the use of a comprehensive information retrieval system, basically of the MEDLARS or ASCA type, geared specifically to the needs of pharmacologists in the UK. This is mainly a clinical and research requirement, could be difficult and costly to establish, and beyond this brief mention must be regarded as outside our terms of reference.

8.2. Stock control in hospitals and general practice

Improved stock control procedures and proper rotation of stock are becoming increasingly important where the effective shelf life of drugs is limited. Considerable effort is now being devoted to this subject in the hospital service. The introduction of ward pharmacy schemes, such as that pioneered in Aberdeen and now being applied in Glasgow, is aimed at reducing over-all stock levels and ensuring satisfactory rotation without reducing availability; it seems to us that this work should be extended to all hospitals as quickly as possible.

The question of stock rotation and shelf life is equally important for the chemists who supply patients from doctors' prescriptions. At present they frequently need to adopt an *ad-hoc* approach to cater for the general but undefined prescribing habits of doctors in their locality.

Much greater use could be made of data already captured on actual consumption. This provides a very ready basis for considering variety reduction and the selection of 'preferred' types of common drugs. Mutual agreement amongst doctors in a locality (or even in the area covered by a current executive council or future health board) to use a preferred list would be of great assistance to chemists in planning stocking procedures. It would not encroach on the clinical freedom of the individual doctor and the resultant procedures could ultimately be integrated with hospital drug selection and supervision at a suitable level when health boards are set up.

In the course of a year over 5,000 different drugs are prescribed by GPs. But 82 per cent of the 28 million prescriptions are accounted for by no more

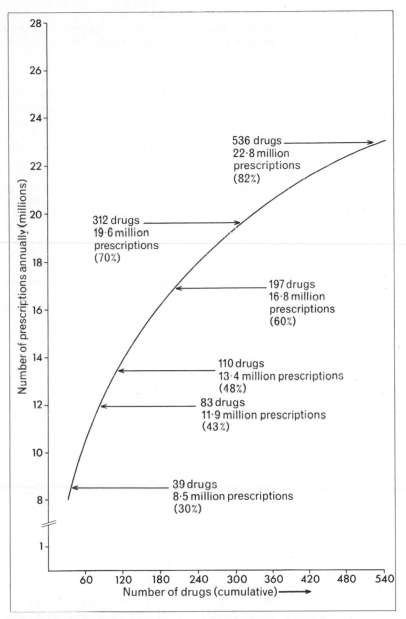

Fig. 8.1. Percentage of prescriptions accounted for by the most commonly prescribed drugs (*Source*. Chief Pharmacist's analysis of prescriptions, based on annual 1 per cent sample)

than 536 drugs and there is a very rapid decline in frequency from the more to the less frequent (see Fig. 8.1). This suggests first that agreement on drugs to be stocked should not be difficult to reach and secondly that automated methods of pricing are long overdue.

8.3. Prescribing levels

The apparent lack of agreement on prescribing levels seems to us both surprising and disturbing. Establishing basic standards of prescription quantity could have a far greater effect on the NHS drug bill than imposition of prescription charges (during 1969 about £1·5 million was recovered by these charges, out of a total cost of prescriptions in general practice of about £20 million). Moreover, many doctors are becoming increasingly concerned about the dangerous hoarding of largely unidentifiable drugs in kitchen and bathroom cabinets. Prescribing 25, 30, or 50 tablets when, for example, one tablet three times a day for a week is required, benefits neither doctor, patient, nor NHS and it is generally believed that small excesses of this type result in a substantial amount of wastage annually.

8.4. Requirements for the future

The NHS needs to have available an analysis of the pattern of prescribing in different localities, of individual doctors, group practices and health centres, and for individual patients or families. This information is required, not with a view to censure of individuals, though this will arise from time to time, but in order to improve the service provided to the public, to help assess the relative merits of different forms of treatment, to monitor and improve ratios of costs, and in extreme cases to ascertain those at risk from previous therapy.

To be able to carry out such operations the NHS needs to have for each prescription, the following data: The drug prescribed, dosage details, the date, patient identity, doctor identity, chemist identity.

The data must be available for each prescription in order to be able to process it in any way which may seem to offer some return by way of research, costs, or early warning. All this data is already captured on prescription forms but needs to be made accessible to analysis.

The Drug Pricing Bureaux manage to process prescription forms for payment of chemists and to carry out some limited analyses, with no aids other than comptometers. They also manage to provide a minimal service associated with the overseeing of prescribing habits and fulfilling prescription exemption requirements. This is no mean achievement, indeed it must be viewed with some wonder, as will be readily acknowledged by anyone who has examined the state of prescription forms and the size and scope of code-books, and has pondered the number (28 million) of prescriptions handled annually. A proper and effective basis for processing prescription data should be introduced as a matter of high priority. A possible organization of a CSA Drugs Group is shown in Fig. 8.2.

However, as long as present methods of writing and pricing prescriptions continue, any attempt to extract management information would be an additional procedure and therefore entail additional expense. Additional expense is unlikely to be welcomed at any time, and certainly not in the present political and economic climate; the alternative would be a change in the procedures for dealing with prescriptions, and in section 12.3 we examine two

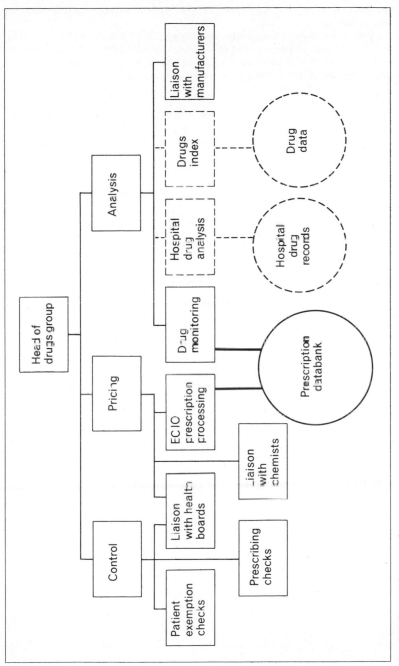

Fig. 8.2. Central drugs services

methods which could provide the data required without incurring additional running expense.

The argument that doctors and chemists will not tolerate changes in their habits seems too negative an approach. Anybody will change his habits if the benefits of doing so (for instance by having less work or being paid more promptly) can be demonstrated in an unequivocal manner.

8.5. Conclusion

The NHS must therefore decide whether or not it wishes to capitalize on the drug information it now holds. If it does, then it must set about the task of transforming the information into a usable form with the minimum of expense and effort and with the maximum of co-operation of doctors and chemists.

9. Buildings and plant

Building works account for about 10 per cent of annual expenditure in the Scottish health service, in other words costs are similar to those incurred on either general supplies or drugs. A building is a permanent asset expected to last for many years and those responsible for building programmes have a difficult task for which they need the best and latest data available.
There are three main purposes for which such data is required:

1. Strategic planning requiring identification of over-all forward requirements. This necessitates analysis of interrelated factors such as morbidity, population movement, general area development plans, environment, and social factors.

2. Specific developments including choice of site, balance of specialties (with existing facilities), staffing, and accessibility.

3. Project planning and control covering a wide range of activities starting with architectural and building work and ending with commissioning of the new facilities.

9.1. Replacements and maintenance
The above are primarily concerned with the development of new facilities and major extension and rebuilding programmes. A completely new building is a comparative rarity and it will also be necessary to have data available for planning routine maintenance and modernization. Indeed, by far the greatest difficulty will in our opinion be presented by the assessment of replacement requirements. Age is not a sufficient criterion on which to base a replacement decision. Age contributes towards inefficiency, in that an older building may cost more in maintenance, may not be suited to modern techniques, or may be sited in an area which has been depopulated. However, any building can have these disadvantages, regardless of age, and it might be more realistic to base the replacement programme on such disadvantages rather than on age alone.
Replacement of major plant is beset with the same kind of problem, that is, it is necessary to find some criteria on which to base replacement decisions. Ultimately the criterion is cost of providing a service; if a new heating plant will provide the service required at lower over-all cost than the existing plant, then there is a good case for replacement.

9.2. Accounting methods
Means must be available for assessing over-all cost, a task which the present accounting methods of the NHS sometimes make difficult. Writing off expenditure in the year in which it is incurred may simplify accounting procedures but it also creates difficulties for those who wish to show that a capital sum spent now will result in savings over the next few years. This can

apply to a complete building, or it can apply to a major item of equipment. Two hospitals reported that they had been trying to obtain sanction for new heating plant for five years. Both claimed that the cost of new plant would have been recovered through reduced fuel costs alone in the course of those five years, without taking into account any reductions in maintenance and repairs which could have been expected. The regional hospital boards concerned were said to be reluctant to spend, say, £50,000 on new plant, because the entire amount would have to be accounted for in one year and could not be spread over those years when there would be consequential savings in running costs.

These examples could be accounted for by differences in perspective between regional hospital boards and boards of management and it is claimed in some quarters that these differences will be removed by the establishment of health boards. Whether they are removed or not, we suggest that financial data should always be made available in a manner which will enable discounted cash flow techniques to be applied. All concerned will then be able to appreciate the global requirements for capital investment rather than confining attention to fulfilment of their own parochial needs.

There is another aspect of accounting practice which may repay examination. NHS buildings occupy some of the most valuable real estate of many major cities and towns but this is not shown on any balance sheet. The necessity of occupying some of these sites is questionable; it is certainly no easier to get to the centre of a large city than to reach the outskirts.

Many small companies have gone into liquidation only to find subsequently that sale of valuable premises in a city centre, *which were not strictly necessary for the conduct of the business*, would have yielded sufficient cash to pay off all creditors and find premises elsewhere. It would be tragic if NHS developments were to be delayed through ignorance of the value of premises in more expensive localities.

It is not suggested that all hospitals or other buildings in city centres should be sold off forthwith and replaced by premises elsewhere, but that it should be made possible to take into account relative land values among many other factors when a building is due for replacement in the normal course of events.

9.3. Data requirements

As with other major areas of data, most of the data required for planning of new and replacement buildings and plant is probably not in a form which would be ideal for the purpose, but at least is available somewhere in the NHS and needs to be presented in a different manner, and processed by different techniques. Some of the data required could be made available as a result of recommendations in Chapters 5-8.

The first requirement is general morbidity data, and we refer back to Figs. 4.1 and 5.1., showing data accumulations at health board level. Some of this data is certainly available now but needs to be related to developments outside the NHS, showing changing patterns of morbidity as social and environmental conditions have changed. A model could then be validated so that when the data is supplemented through research and intelligence activities with predictions on medical achievements (for instance, development of new treatment methods or changes in NHS objectives), and changes in environment (for instance, motorway construction or urban redevelopment) a picture of future requirements can be obtained. Major projects span many years and the requirement of assessing future demand cannot be over-emphasized.

The second requirement is data on existing buildings. This can be summarized as follows:

9.3.1. *Basic data*
Location; site area; floor area; number of floors; date erected, and extensions; replacement year; condition; when assessed; revised replacement year; current use; restrictions on use.

9.3.2. *Plant*
Power units—type, size, output; lifts; communications (pneumatic tubes, telephones, closed-circuit TV).

9.3.3. *Environment*
Public transport; parking; recreation facilities; waiting-rooms; refreshments.

9.3.4. *Staffing requirements*
Normal running; emergency basis; care and maintenance only.

The manner in which this data is expressed is all-important. As an example, there is little value in simply knowing that public transport is available. The rate at which present public transport can deliver people to the main entrance must be known together with the potential for increased capacity at prescribed hours of the day, should this be required.

The third requirement is data on regular maintenance schedules and costs. The cost of fuel per in-patient week is irrelevant to a decision on whether to install a new heating unit: the data required is total cost of heating, including manpower, repairs and spares, to keep the building at the required temperature.

9.4. Conclusion
Buildings and plant are long-term investments and need to be viewed in the light of future requirements as well as the present. It should be ensured that accounting practices of the NHS will facilitate proper assessment of capital equipment programmes.

Much of the data required by planners should be available already, and most of the remainder will be available if recommendations set out in Chapters 5-8 are implemented. This will need to be supplemented by research and intelligence activity on future medical and environmental progress.

10. Other databanks

In this study we have concentrated our attention on the main activities of the NHS and given particular emphasis to those areas which account for the major portion of NHS costs. However, in a complex organization providing a wide range of services, there are many lower-volume data-collection and transmission activities which are vital to the proper functioning of the service. These must be studied at some stage and a suitable basis of working has to be established to meet the needs of the new administrative structure. In some cases it may be necessary to establish links with the main stream of information flow and main databanks. In particular, ophthalmic, blood transfusion and ambulance services, provision of artificial limbs and surgical appliances, and the communication of data on infectious (communicable) diseases will all require attention.

10.1. Ophthalmic services
The main activities are:

a. The recording and payment for ophthalmic services provided outside the hospital service.

b. Recording and linking of medical data on all aspects of ophthalmic care.

c. Registration of blind persons.

10.2. Blood transfusions
Records of blood donors are maintained at a number of centres and there are recall procedures in operation. Links with health boards for blood donors' records could therefore be valuable since each member of this special group of people will have an up-to-date record at one health board.

10.3. Ambulance services
An operational research study on the ambulance service is now in progress. It may be necessary to establish formal routine recording of data on patterns of ambulance activity for planning forward policy and negotiating pay and conditions of service.

10.4. Disabled and handicapped persons
At present hospitals carry out amputations and prescribe artificial limbs and surgical appliances, a branch of the SHHD Supplies Division controls the provisioning of artificial limbs and local authorities maintain registers of disabled and handicapped persons. No formal links exist between these activities and the recording and communication of data is done on an *ad-hoc* basis. Establishment of more formal links and identification of responsibility for co-ordinating the transmission of data will have to be considered under the new structure. A particularly important point is the requirement of the 1970

Act obliging local authorities to maintain a disabled and handicapped persons' register.

10.5. Communicable diseases

The present arrangements for communicating information on infectious diseases involve many parts of the NHS. Data is communicated from the periphery (GPs, laboratories, and hospitals) and at various stages goes to MOHs, the Communicable Diseases Centre, and the GRO.

The flow of data and the maintenance of records will need to be reviewed when GPs, laboratories, hospitals, and the successors to MOHs are all administered within a unified structure.

10.6. Specialized centres

In some areas of medical care a small number of highly specialized centres serve the needs for Scotland as a whole. In these cases arrangements will need to be made to cross-link the flow of information between different health boards. Although the volume of data will be relatively small, appropriate attention to recording and aggregating data on incidence of morbidity patterns by area of origin could be of considerable value in the longer-term expansion of specialized facilities.

11. Information services

In other sections of this report we have discussed the capture and presentation of data for management and administrative functions, the need to seek standardization over a much broader front than hitherto, and the kind of data required. The establishment, maintenance, and development of an information service is an important and highly specialized function in its own right and this chapter is concerned specifically with the activities inherent in this function.

11.1. Three major activities

It is possible to envisage a wide variety of activities being undertaken by an information services group but basically they can be resolved into two major divisions—data processing and research and statistics. Research and statistics could itself be broken down into research and intelligence (a function already recognized in the SHHD) and publications and statistics. These two possible subdivisions are discussed first, and then follows a discussion of the data-processing function.

11.1.1. *Research and intelligence*

Two main streams of research can be distinguished—one with a medical or at least epidemiological bias and one with an operational bias to include such activities as organization and method study and work study.

There is also a third function which properly belongs to research and intelligence. This is scientific intelligence, or the investigation of techniques and equipment developed in industry, government, or the universities with a view to their adaptation and application in the NHS.

The Research and Intelligence Unit of the SHHD currently undertakes or supports a variety of epidemiological research work and it has a fairly small branch for research into the working of the NHS and conduct of general surveys. It was also responsible for commissioning the study which led to this report. Joint research and intelligence units have also been established by universities and regional hospital boards to co-ordinate work at the periphery.

The scientific intelligence function at present seems to be split between various branches with of course substantial contributions from a number of medical groups. The Western Regional Hospital Board has established its own Department of Clinical Physics and Bio-engineering. If research and intelligence is to be carried out with maximum effectiveness close liaison with the scientific intelligence functions will certainly be desirable and it may be necessary to recognize the fact in any formal organization structure.

11.1.2. *Publications and statistics*

Dissemination of information can be either within the NHS or to the public in general. In either case, however, there are a number of activities to be brought together, such as:

a. Provision of operational data to doctors, administrators, and functional groups in the CSA, for example, output from SMR 1 processing, analyses of drug use, and profiles of the personnel position.

b. Annual provision of statistics for public, parliamentary, and NHS comment and question.

c. Publication of advice in the form of booklets and pamphlets on health.

d. Advertising, such as that on the dangers of smoking, pep pills, and hazards to children.

In addition the public should be better informed on administrative and operational arrangements of the NHS, for instance on when to contact the GP rather than visit the hospital casualty department, on the importance of advising changes of address and registering with a new doctor as soon as possible after moving to a new district, and on the availability of a prescription season ticket.

Some of these activities are now carried out by the Statistics Branches of the Research and Intelligence Unit, some by the Health Education Unit, some by the division dealing with General Medical Services, and some by the Scottish Information Office. The public are informed of the need to advise changes of address and re-register with a new doctor merely by a note appearing on the medical card.

Those activities currently carried out in the Research and Intelligence Unit would form part of any research and statistics division of an information services group, while close liaison would be required with health education and advertising groups.

11.1.3. *Data processing*

This is the essential supporting activity to all others. It is concerned not only with data processing but also with data capture, information retrieval techniques, and the use of computers. It must therefore have available knowledge and skills in computer hardware and software, procedures, data transmission, packages, and office equipment in general.

This part of the group must be able to advise the research and statistics division whether data required for an investigation is already available, can be made available easily, or will need a special collection exercise and must be able to devise methods of presenting information in the form required by that division. It should also be ready to take the initiative in proposing new methods of presentation.

Close contact will be required with other groups of the CSA and the Data-Processing Division should be capable of supplying them with the expertise required for development of data systems, by formation of multidisciplinary teams.

Like research and statistics, the data-processing function is a fragmented activity at present, some processing of data being carried out by the SOCS but other aspects being scattered throughout the NHS, insofar as they are attended to at all.

The SHHD has one small branch with the specific responsibility of computer policy and development.

11.2. The central structure

Fig. 11.1 shows how these activities might be organized as a group of the CSA. Two major divisions are shown which we suggest be headed by a chief research officer, and a chief information processing officer. Activities which are similar are brought together under the same officer who will then be able to direct them purposefully and in a co-ordinated manner.

A third activity has been included to allow for liaison with the GRO and the NHSCR. This will certainly not be the only liaison required: the necessity for liaison with scientific intelligence units, health education, and publications has already been discussed above, and the necessity for constant interpretation of data, intelligence, and opinion has been referred to in Chapter 4.

11.3. Information services within the Common Services Agency

The information services group would have important services to provide to other central groups. It would be expected to help a personnel group and supplies group to develop their systems, and to present information in the most relevant manner whether this were in the form of tables, charts, graphs, or histograms.

The information services group would provide a special type of expertise, but could not be expected to provide all the staff required for development of, for instance, manpower planning or supplies forecasting. For either of these activities it would be necessary to form multidisciplinary teams, consisting in the first case of data-processing staff, behavioural scientists, operations research staff, personnel officers, and senior representatives of the particular profession for which the study is being carried out. The development of supplies forecasting would require data-processing, operations research, and supplies group staff and it might be necessary in the case of some items of supply to second further specialist staff, for instance a doctor, a nurse, or a catering officer to the project team.

It is most important to understand the functioning of the multidisciplinary team. The team leader has a dual responsibility, first to the users of the system being developed, to ensure that they are provided with the system they require, and secondly to the information services group, to ensure that the system is developed and will operate in as efficient a manner as possible.

For the duration of the project the members of the team are responsible to the project team leader, but their permanent line of reporting remains to their own 'home' division or group. At the conclusion of a project the team is disbanded and each member returns to his 'home' posting.

The concept is not new, nor is it confined to information systems development; it has been adopted in many large organizations, for instance for product development, or to ensure a smooth relocation of a company to new premises; there are similarities also in some aspects of SHHD working, for instance, in the provision of medical and nursing experience to the manpower planning unit.

11.4. The information services group and the National Health Service

We have discussed in sections 11.1 and 11.3 the nature of the specialist and advisory role that information services have to play. They also have a most important co-ordinating, supervisory, and control function.

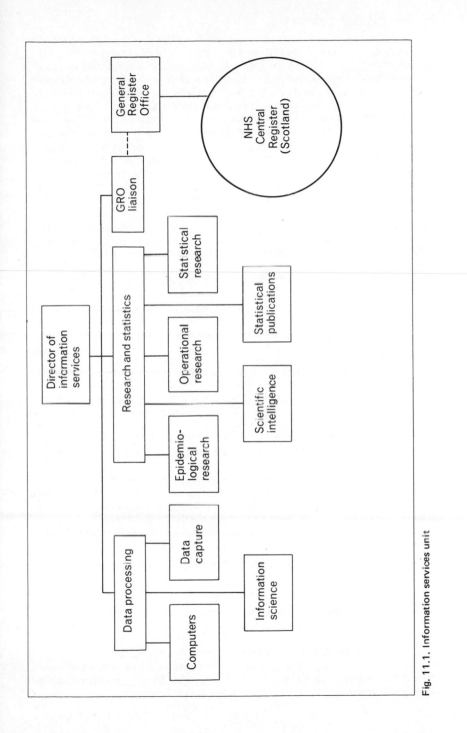

Fig. 11.1. Information services unit

The advantage of standardized approaches to the development of information services is discussed in Chapter 15. A standardized approach implies a unified activity, permeating the entire NHS structure; information services will need to be developed at health board and unit level, to provide the same kind of service to specialists in community medicine, hospitals, and clinical divisions as they will provide to other groups in the CSA.

The objectives of an information service are to optimise the ability to provide information with the cost of collecting, storing, and retrieving the data. An information services group would therefore have a difficult and delicate task, striking the correct balance between routine collection of data in anticipation of requirements and special collection exercises to answer particular kinds of inquiry. It would be required to extract any routine data which is wanted centrally, for instance selected patient, manpower, or drugs data, but it is inevitable that it would also frequently be faced with collection of non-routine data, for instance to support a survey or an individual research project. A constant review of activities would be required, to ensure that the scope of routine data collection continued to reflect the demands which were being made of the data.

Some idea of the kind of problems can be gained from two current situations. There are five regional hospital boards, each with its payroll system. It should be possible to guarantee that any data which may be required centrally will be available from each of the five payroll files. If the required data is available it should be possible to guarantee that it will be in compatible form, and that each file will have the same degree of accuracy.

The second example is form HS 10, a return by each hospital board of management on bed statistics and discharges during the preceding six months. It would be astonishing to anyone unfamiliar with the working of the NHS to learn that there is no standard HS 10 form but a large number of incompatible formats, so that extracting data from the entire range of HS 10 forms is a precarious undertaking. In fact, the Committee for the Review of Non-diagnostic Statistics has gone so far as to give special attention to form HS 10, to try and put some semblance of uniformity into its format, preparation, and submission.

These difficulties have arisen during a period when there have been five regional hospital boards. By itself, the substitution of fourteen health boards could actually increase the difficulties. If optimization of service and cost is to be achieved, a rationalization of existing methods of data collection, storage, processing, and retrieval is essential. An information services group would need to be armed with authority on three main issues:

a. To lay down standards within which the local information services will operate.

b. To assign scarce information processing staff to the best advantage.

c. To demand the data required centrally, irrespective of whether this is available from regularly held files or requires special collection.

11.5. Relationships with other bodies

The necessity to distinguish the roles of two other bodies was mentioned in Chapter 3. These are the Scottish Office Computer Services and the Scottish Advisory Committee on Computers in the Health Service.

11.5.1. *Scottish Office Computer Services (SOCS)*

SOCS has accumulated valuable experience of NHS data-processing activities such as SMR 1, Dental Estimates Board, research work, and superannuation. However, there are three aspects of the organization of SOCS which need to be borne in mind:

a. Health service computing work is competing with other Scottish Office activities and irrespective of scheduling procedures at SOCS, may not always receive the priority which is thought desirable for the NHS.

b. In addition to NHS records SOCS deals with data for a number of other government departments. Viewed from outside, that is the public, it may well seem that a breach of confidentiality could occur. This is in no way a reflection on the integrity of SOCS staff but must be seen in the context of present public apprehension regarding databanks.

c. SOCS was set up to bring together in one organization the data-processing facilities formerly provided by separate departments of the Secretary of State for Scotland (one of which is the SHHD) and so achieve the economies of scale not otherwise possible. NHS computing activities have now increased significantly and in conjunction with the future reorganization it seems appropriate to consider the need for separate facilities.

For these reasons we recommend that whilst every opportunity should be taken to draw upon the past experience of SOCS it should not be part of the managerial and administrative data system of the future health service. Complete independence from SOCS will obviously take time to achieve but this should be the aim of the information services.

11.5.2. *Scottish Advisory Committee on Computers in the Health Service (SACCHS)*

This committee was established to advise the Secretary of State and NHS authorities on the use of computers in the health service in Scotland. It has to date considered general policy, has established some working groups on such topics as file structure, and has had referred to it a number of individual projects which would require the use of a computer.

The future requirements of the NHS will call for more formal control and forward planning of expenditure on computer developments and a suitable basis could be formulated from the recommendations of the Flowers Committee (11) which dealt with the policy and financing of computers for research. A working relationship will be required between an information services group and SACCHS with the latter developing its early work to advise on the following:

a. A policy on compatibility of computer hardware in the NHS and the provision of computer facilities at all levels.

b. A policy on software compatibility to ensure that the widest range of programmes becomes available at all levels and that duplication of effort and cost is eliminated except in the case of controlled experiments.

c. Extension of the concept of working groups on items of major importance and priority, ensuring these groups give maximum attention to experience already gained in commerce, industry, and the universities.

11.6. The use of statistical returns

Much of the data now available to NHS authorities is pre-digested in the form of statistics at an early stage, that is to say certain items are related to other items in a predefined manner of source. Cross-relating this data to relevant data from other sources is thereby inhibited. Often rather arbitrary units and ratios are derived, for instance cleaning costs per 1,000 ft^2. These allow easy superficial comparisons to be made, but make a limited contribution to efficient utilization of resources.

Many people, whether concerned with preparation or use of statistical data of this kind, are aware of its shortcomings for management, planning, and research purposes. Unfortunately such data is often at present the only source of information available.

Routine completion of periodic returns on such matters as staff complements (forms HS 7 and HS 8) and bed statistics (HS 10) could be avoided if the databanks discussed in other sections of this report were established. Tabular output could still be made available if required and it should already be possible to compile HS 7 and HS 8 returns from payroll files (the South-eastern Regional Hospital Board claims some success with this). This approach should be encouraged: the volume of routine published statistics can be significantly reduced by developing a flow of basic data on relevant activities.

11.7. Data storage and information retrieval

A system is required in which basic individual records are the main source of on-going information. These records can be brought together as necessary to form databanks which individuals can access in a variety of ways both for routine appraisals and random inquiries.

This is not to deny that there will in the NHS be a continuing need to prepare and present statistics for the following purposes:

a. To provide a readily available source of data for parliamentary, press, and public appraisal.

b. To maintain compatibility with other health departments on aggregated data relating to morbidity, mortality, and general health services activity.

Any organization needs to make routine periodic assessments of activity and indeed a feature of information retrieval systems is the ability to generate regular reports.

Report generation on a routine basis must, however, form only part of the activity of an information system: it should be supported by an interrogation capability to provide facilities for follow-up inquiries of the 'tell me more' kind and random inquiries of the 'what is the position' kind. More specifically the main requirements of an NHS information system can be summarized as follows:

a. To interrogate data records to answer both specific and general questions as they arise. This provides a means of monitoring past and current activity at local through to national level.

b. To generate periodic reports from basic data records for:

(i) Preparation of recall and review lists.

(ii) Provision of planning data and identification of long-term trends.

(iii) Preparation of general statistics.

The medical side of the NHS has recognized the need for a more effective information system and the development of hospital discharge data processing (SMR 1) is a step towards what is required across all areas of interest and activity. The intrinsic value of the basic discharge records passing upwards through the system has already been demonstrated and appreciated. Regular reports are generated and an increasing number of *ad-hoc* analyses are being carried out at the request of individual hospital consultants. However, the immediate aim should be to improve the data capture arrangements so that the maximum benefit can be derived from the data.

The basic principles on which this project is based can be adopted over a much wider range of activities. The gathering of data records and their upward flow through the different levels of the organization must gradually replace the process of periodic statistical reporting from the bottom. Standardization of software is discussed in Chapter 15 and information retrieval processing packages are no exception. We consider that the service would save time and money by developing two computer program packages for interrogation of the various databanks, namely a general-purpose report generator and an iterative record search package as suggested in Appendix 3 of Scicon's report on commodity coding for the National Computing Centre (12). We recommend that the information services group of the CSA should be responsible for design development and implementation of these packages once detailed feasibility has been established.

11.8. Summary

The various activities concerned with research, intelligence, and information need to be brought together into a single entity. This group should provide services for the entire NHS, both in developing and controlling standardized systems.

The keynote is flexibility. The collection of predigested statistics should be eschewed and for them should be substituted basic data records which can be accessed in a variety of ways by users at different levels of the organization.

12. Phasing of developments

In previous chapters we have discussed functions and data requirements of the future NHS. We have also made some references to the need to begin development of the procedures required for the new organization.

We now turn to detailed consideration of problems which will have to be overcome during the next few years if a viable data system is to be developed. The most obvious point to be considered is that the complexity of the required developments will necessitate thorough planning and careful control in order to make full use of available resources, particularly the skilled manpower essential for sophisticated long-range developments. All organizations have to overcome considerable difficulties in order to develop new systems: in the NHS these difficulties are compounded by the state of flux in the organization itself and not least by the fact that there exists no group comparable to the information services group described in Chapter 11 which could take charge of a development programme.

In the following three sections, therefore, an attempt is made to isolate first problems stemming from the lack of clear delineation of the functions of the future organization (12.1), secondly those stemming from the lack of correspondence between current authorities and proposed authorities, whether in terms of function, geographical area, or reporting structure (12.2) and thirdly the problems to be expected in detailed development work (12.3). We then offer a method of working which we believe to be practicable (12.4).

12.1. Organizational considerations

The function and operation of a particular organization will change. This change may arise from an increase in volume of business or the development of a new kind of business; it may arise through the adoption of new processes or techniques, or a change in the personnel which, even if it occurs at an apparently low level can affect working relationships both inside and outside the organization.

Occasionally a formal restructuring of an organization may be carried out which necessitates total reorganization of operations, but which in other cases may only be belated recognition of the real situation. The formal restructuring of the NHS in Scotland which is currently being planned is a combination of both these elements. There are already examples of co-operation between different sectors of the NHS, for instance in existing health centres, or the close links formed between universities and GPs for some specific programmes and between local authorities and GPs for immunization programmes. Restructuring will give formal recognition to these co-operative undertakings but it will also entail the complete reorganization of other activities which have not so far been integrated. Additionally there will be changes of function and responsibility which more closely reflect the nature of the services to be provided by the NHS of the 1970s and 1980s.

A fixed point, usually referred to as defined requirements or 'frozen' specifications is usually regarded as a prerequisite of system development: in this case future changes are normally definable to a reasonable degree and are catered for where appropriate by 'provision for expansion' or 'ease of modification'. However, the structure of the NHS above and below health board level has not yet been specified nor have the precise responsibilities of groups of functionally oriented staff been defined in detail. It is not therefore possible to begin from a fixed, well-defined organization and this has serious implications for the development of an effective information system. The elusiveness of the target will impose flexibility on any systems proposed. Thus it may be necessary to incorporate additional data into the system, to retrieve information by new axes of search, and to make information available at different levels and places without the necessity for reorganization of the basic system.

What can be clearly identified, however, are the three main data priorities which must be kept in mind when reorganizing the NHS and developing an improved information system. These are as follows:

12.1.1. First priority
Functional data (i.e. data which is directly associated with functional activities) such as:

a. Processing of prescription data to pay chemists.

b. Maintenance of doctors' lists to pay doctors.

c. Ordering and paying for supplies for the hospital service.

12.1.2. Second priority
Management data (i.e. data which is used to monitor the various functional activities and assess both current and future needs). This includes:

a. Collection and processing of data on staff.

b. Collection and processing of all morbidity data.

12.1.3. Third priority
Research data, which covers a wide variety of projects in all branches and at all levels of the NHS. It also includes the various developments and exploratory ad-hoc exercises.

A considerable effort will be necessary to reorganize the detailed work currently carried out by 5 regional hospital boards, 25 executive councils, 56 local authorities, and a number of special units. A smooth transition to 14 health boards will only be achieved by extensive advance planning to reallocate buildings, manpower, patients, and functional activities among the new authorities: this will demand up-to-date data and working procedures.

A further examination of Fig. 3.1 is appropriate at this point as it shows clearly that developments must be put in hand while the present structure is in existence. We are most perturbed at the lack of urgency, indeed complacency, which pervades all levels of the service. The majority of people we have interviewed have found great difficulty in projecting themselves forward into the health board setting: many seem to view the reorganization purely as a 'name-changing' operation. One of the results of this feeling is that substantial effort is being devoted to a wide variety of *ad-hoc* developments in data collection and processing which could be irrelevant to the organization to be introduced in the next few years. Examples are the allocation of new regional numbers and issue of plastic identification cards by the Eastern Regional Hospital Board, and central revision of HS 10 forms and development of staff engagement forms. This kind of work should be reviewed and where appropriate adopted on an all-Scotland basis; the effort and resources previously devoted to *ad-hoc* developments need to be redirected to identifying the information requirements of health boards.

Ultimately a full-scale method study or organization study will be required to delineate the functional requirements of the organization. Every procedure will have to be examined in detail, responsibilities will have to be clearly defined, and wherever an information system is to be computer-based it will be necessary to undertake much more thorough systems investigation and design, to program general-purpose modules, and eventually to install hardware facilities. The resulting system will undoubtedly differ significantly from a rigid system developed to serve the fixed requirements which can be defined now. The investment in skills must be made at the right end of developments—the beginning—and the investment in hardware must support a steady expansion of the total systems in operation.

It is not possible to construct a data system which will answer all the questions all of the time. It is not possible or necessarily desirable to attempt to define completely the detailed requirements of a data system. The principles can be stated, some obvious requirements can be identified and used as a starting-point and a framework can then be built which will allow continuous development. The notion of flexibility must be firmly implanted in the minds of everyone connected with data system development; the overheads of flexibility must be accepted.

12.2. Operational considerations

The five main areas which at the present time can be clearly seen to need development are patient data, staff, drugs, supplies, and capital programmes. Patient data is discussed first as it is the base from which requirements of the other four may be predicted; the remaining four are the functions which are major consumers of NHS finance.

Each of the major areas of data needs to be examined to determine the most effective application of resources. For patient, or person, data there is an urgent need to establish the methods for reallocation to health boards and to begin the task of reallocation itself. The assistance of 5 regional hospital boards, 25 executive councils, and 56 local health authorities will have to be sought and this is in itself no easy task. Two main avenues of development can be explored:

a. The establishment of a basic register of people from executive council records: this should be extended by the addition of relevant items from the various national, regional, and local registers for special groups such as the blind, handicapped persons, and so on.

b. The devolution of hospital discharge form (SMR 1) processing to existing regional computing facilities and subsequent linking of discharge data with the basic register.

Both these seemingly straightforward developments are fraught with difficulties, the former because of the transition from one organization to another, the latter because of the need to ensure maintenance of standards at all links in the processing chain. The rewards, however, could be great for, in addition to providing a sound basis for patient data in health boards, successful consolidation of registers and in-patient data would ease the subsequent introduction of a feasible scheme for capturing out-patient data (an out-patient equivalent of SMR 1).

Personnel data on the other hand would be more effectively tackled on a national scale. The existing reporting systems on administrative, clerical, and nursing staff could provide a manpower planning unit with all the data required initially for medium- and long-range planning. Should there be any doubts about the confidential nature of such data, it would not be necessary for this purpose to pass names forward from the reporting system; longer-range planning is primarily concerned with age distributions, clusters of retirements, recruitment patterns, and the general availability and demand for manpower in different grades, both nationally and by area.

The NHS does not at present have a personnel management structure which could make use of more detailed data; if, however, the recommended personnel function emerges under the new organization, it will be able to use the data mentioned above as a basis for a more comprehensive development in training, career guidance, and promotion.

Supplies, other than drugs, must basically be tackled on a national scale because it is at the centre that initial decisions must be taken about those items to be supplied against central contracts and the procedures to be adopted by area boards and local management. However, much of the data required is accumulated locally and co-operation will have to be obtained from a number of regional hospital boards and boards of management. At first it might be perfectly adequate to accumulate data on the names of suppliers of a particular item, its specification, unit quantity, and prevailing price, with usage distribution where available. For the more complex equipment a separate information retrieval system through which scientific and technical papers could be traced would be extremely valuable but such systems are expensive and difficult to establish and this is a decision for the authority responsible for advising on selection of equipment. Whatever system is decided upon for different classes of items, hard data on demand will be needed but it must be supported by a continuing activity of market intelligence. A well-organized and well-informed system of control must be generated to exploit the very considerable purchasing power of the NHS.

Prescriptions are already processed centrally for payment purposes and for some limited analyses. The payment processing cycle could be incorporated into a general managerial function. Recording of prescriptions against individual medical records is another possibility but this would pose considerable problems of data capture, if done at the doctor level, or data transfer, if derived from prescription processing.

Capital investment programmes should continue on an *ad-hoc* basis and might even continue on that basis indefinitely. Much of the data required for initial investment decisions will be obtained from operational procedures, for instance, fuel and power costs for a particular plant, or maintenance costs for a building, against which must be set costs of providing new plant or buildings.

Standards of provisioning have been set up for some departments and should be developed so that the full costs of a new building or unit can be more easily assessed. During lengthy development periods project status should be readily ascertainable and the use made of critical path techniques should be extended. The opening of a new hospital has far-reaching consequences for patients, staff, transport, suppliers, and public utilities, all of whom need to be supplied with accurate up-to-date information.

12.3. Development considerations

It is self evident that even the superficially simple developments described in the preceding section will not happen of their own accord. Each must be planned, and its problems identified, including changed responsibilities and opposition to change. A steady growth in momentum must be maintained right through development and into the operational days of the new procedures.

The developments will not be made any easier by the absence of a strong professionally staffed information services group and a number of *ad-hoc* arrangements, such as are described in section 12.4 will be required. It may be of assistance if we illustrate, with the aid of simple networks, some of the ways in which developments may progress.

12.3.1. *Patient data*

It will be necessary for each health board to accumulate data from its population; a basic register can be set up by drawing on records already available in the executive councils and this has been discussed in Chapter 5 of this report. There are three main problems which must be examined.

a. The proposed health boards do not geographically match existing executive councils and regional hospital boards, consequently it will be necessary to 'reallocate' patients. This must be done in advance by examining existing lists and entering a health board allocation on each record.

b. Doctors' lists are heavily inflated and need to be purged before reallocation.

c. Many records are incomplete in some respect and will need to be augmented.

A substantial effort will be necessary to carry out this work and prepare records for a basic health board patient register. An unco-ordinated approach could prove not only expensive but also ineffective and we recommend that a pilot exercise be carried out for one executive council which could be used as a model for the remainder.

Co-operation should be invited from regional hospital boards and executive councils as a matter of some urgency so that developments can start. The most important consideration initially will be to establish a procedure for cleaning up doctors' lists and the approach adopted must also be suitable for future maintenance of the lists. Development of procedures for notifying all types of change, including simple changes of address, will take time and will entail co-operation between the executive council, doctors, and the public. Close liaison will be required with the GRO to ensure that any procedures developed will be compatible with requirements for maintaining the NHSCR.

A second important stage in the pilot exercise will be to extend the basic executive council records to include data identifying patients who are currently registered in various categories such as blind, cancer, and diabetics.

Thirdly a procedure should be developed for linking other data (such as SMR 1) to these basic records.

When a satisfactory basis has been established and applied to the records of one executive council it should be extended to the remainder. A network of the activities is given in Fig. 12.1.

12.3.2. Personnel

The Scottish Hospital Administrative Staffs Committee (SHASC) collects an annual report on some 750 administrative staff and the Scottish Nursing Staffs Committee (SNSC) has begun to collect annual reports on qualified nurses (at present limited to grades 9, 8, and 7 in hospitals which have implemented the Salmon (7) proposals). A similar system though decentralized is in operation for clerical staff. The collection of similar data for other staff should in our view be initiated: we have discussed this in Chapter 6.

The forms collected by SHASC and SNSC contain most of the basic information which would be required for elementary manpower planning exercises but a method of extracting the relevant items of information from these records would be needed. The manpower planning unit would also require data about wastage and rates of growth and thus would need some historical data.

For administrative staff, provision of historical data should be fairly straightforward as the reporting system has now been in operation for four years; the SNSC, however, has only recently been established and data on nurses and other staff would have to be collected from other sources. It may be possible to obtain some historical data from existing payroll files as a short-term measure.

The laborious examination of payroll files which this would entail could serve other purposes also. The network shown in Fig. 12.2 assumes that an integrated personnel service would be developed, one of the functions of which would be payroll. If an integrated personnel service could be brought into being concurrently with the establishment of health boards much confusion would be avoided but to do this would require a very painstaking exercise over the next few years.

12.3.3. Supplies

In Chapter 7 we have discussed changes in procurement necessary to achieve better value from supplies. There are three main factors to be considered in the development of a supplies system:

a. A greater degree of central contracting and the consequent establishment of closer working links down to unit level would be required.

b. Continuity of contractual arrangements would have to be maintained during the reorganization.

c. Arrangements for procurement now made separately by regional hospital boards, executive councils, and local authorities would have to be integrated.

To overcome these problems we recommend the following:

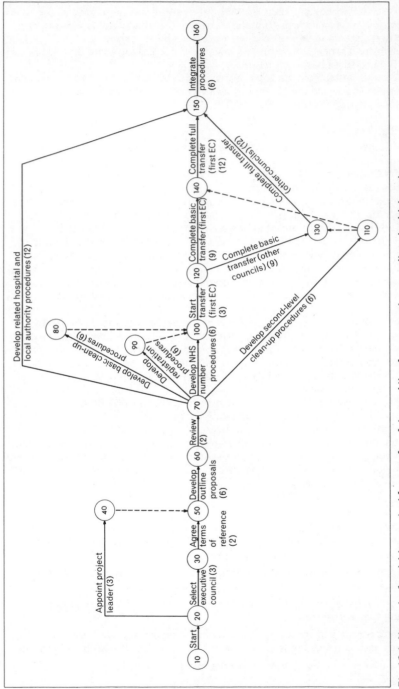

Fig. 12.1. Network of activities required for transfer of doctors' lists from executive councils to health boards

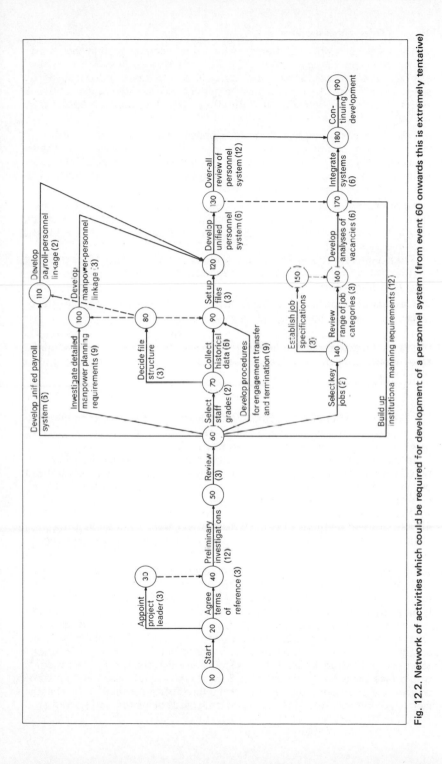

Fig. 12.2. Network of activities which could be required for development of a personnel system (from event 60 onwards this is extremely tentative)

a. That a central supplies authority be set up as recommended in the report on hospital supplies organization (10) with its authority flexible enough to embrace requirements for executive councils and that part of local authority procurement that will ultimately come under the integrated organization. We assume that this authority would ultimately form the supplies group of the CSA.

b. That contracts for locally obtained supplies, such as eggs, milk, fresh vegetables, etc., should continue to be arranged at unit level as a temporary arrangement. (Any collective contracts for such supplies arranged by regional hospital boards should be devolved to a unit basis at an appropriate time before the proposed reorganization takes place.)

c. All other contracts arranged by regional hospital boards should be transferred to the central supplies group at an appropriate time before reorganization. This could be done as they fall due for renewal in the year leading up to implementation of the new organization.

These temporary local and central arrangements would continue until the next renewal of contract at which time the supplies group would decide the basis for future contracts.

d. The central authority should also arrange to take over or renew contracts placed by executive councils and local authorities.

The network provided in Fig. 12.3 assumes that efforts would be concentrated on important selected items. It does not take account of the administrative developments described above, which are assumed to be taking place in parallel.

12.3.4. *Drugs*

The case for a national drug databank has been argued in Chapter 8 but it is also necessary to investigate its possible method of establishment. Fig. 12.4 illustrates a possible development plan (see p. 70).

In this field the method of data capture needs the most serious examination. Processing of prescriptions for payment purposes is already centralized but the lack of adequate machinery makes it extremely difficult to extract information for managerial purposes. The 1968 report by Treasury O & M staff (13) rejected prescription pricing as a computer application on grounds of cost, but two methods of data capture need careful evaluation as they could make the benefits realizable without incurring increases in running costs.

a. The use of embossed plastic cards and recording devices by doctors and chemists could enable all patient, doctor, chemist, and drug data to be captured at source. Each GP would need a recording device of the kind commonly used for credit-card applications. The device would have a fixed plate containing the doctor's name and number. He would also keep one embossed card for each patient, containing name, address, and NHS number. The doctor would emboss his own and the patient's details on each prescription form, write the drug details as he does now and sign the form. The patient would take the form to the chemist. Each chemist would also have a recording device, of a more elaborate nature, with a fixed plate containing the chemist's name and number, space for embossed drug cards or plates, and possibly a

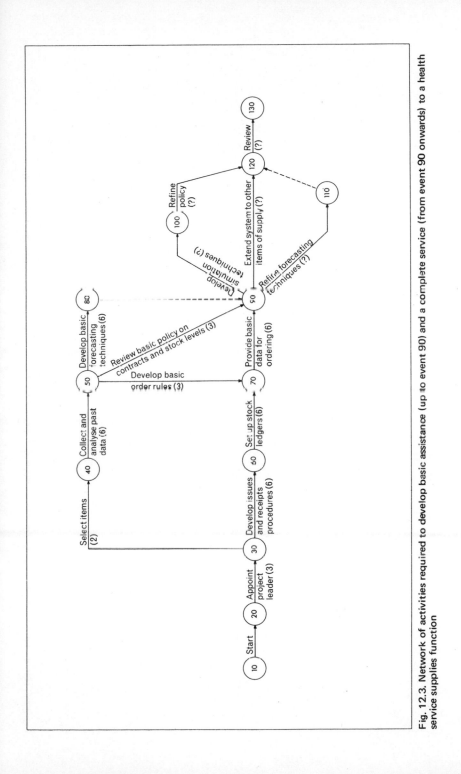

Fig. 12.3. Network of activities required to develop basic assistance (up to event 90) and a complete service (from event 90 onwards) to a health service supplies function

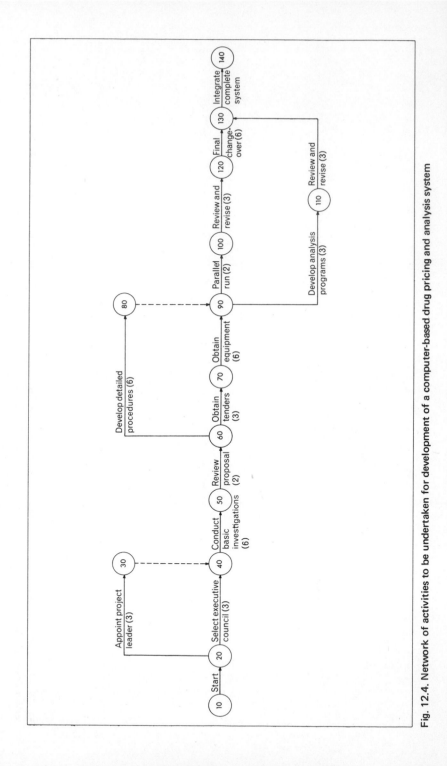

Fig. 12.4. Network of activities to be undertaken for development of a computer-based drug pricing and analysis system

limited number of movable keys. The chemist would insert the prescription form in the recording device, with the appropriate drug card or plate, in order to record chemist and drug details. If keys were available some form of dosage recording could also be established. The prescription form would then be sent to the Drug Pricing Bureau which would convert it into computer input by means of a scanner.

This method of prescribing would require a change in recording habits by doctors and chemists. It would also necessitate redesign of the prescription form. The advantages are:

(i) Writing by doctors is reduced to a minimum, but the doctor still signs the prescription form.

(ii) Writing by chemists is also reduced and could be almost entirely eliminated if part of the redesigned prescription form could itself constitute the container label.

(iii) Most of the central clerical effort is eliminated.

(iv) Data would be captured in machine-processable form.

b. The Drug Pricing Bureau could itself install a small dedicated computer system, with a number of local visual display units each with a keyboard. Entry of drug data would be by a single-choice menu selection method, such as is under development by some hospitals and mail-order establishments, but it would be necessary to enter patient and doctor details by manual keyboard. The advantages of this method are:

(i) Little change in doctors' recording habits would be required, but to take full advantage of the system the patient's NHS number should appear on the prescription form.

(ii) No change in chemists' recording habits would be necessary.

(iii) The system would offer flexibility to cope with policy changes. Once application problems had been overcome, and assuming terminal prices were reduced, it would be possible to install the visual display units in chemists' or doctors' premises.

The two approaches are quite different and would require evaluation by pilot studies before any firm decision about adoption of either could be taken.

12.4. Suggested approach

Detailed planning must begin now if the basis of an information system is to be provided by 1974. In Figs. 12.1-12.4 the figures in parentheses under each activity are estimates of the number of months' duration of the activities, assuming sufficient manpower is available. We do not consider these estimates to be exaggerated, yet only the development of the computer-based drug pricing system is estimated to be completed in less than three years (31 months). Purely basic developments in the supplies field could be completed in 21 months with attention then being concentrated on long-term development of techniques.

It is hoped that presentation through networks will highlight the urgency of the situation. We are aware of the difficulties often encountered when attempting to set up experiments or launch developments; in fact the first of the two experimental approaches to prescription processing was suggested in

Focus on Medical Computer Development (14) and it is disappointing to have to record that no action has so far been possible.

Until an information services group of the kind described in Chapter 11 can be established each development will in our opinion require two levels of expertise, namely a review body and a work-force. The first requirement could be met by appointing a steering committee of interested parties. Such a committee, meeting quarterly or more often if appropriate, would be able to ensure that developments are continuing to move forward at the right speed and in the right direction. The nature of the work, however, calls for frequent contact with the operational authorities concerned and periods of intensive development thinking; we consider therefore that a committee would not be able to do the work itself. A committee could not work to the required level of detail, nor could such a task be undertaken on a part-time basis by staff with other commitments. Full-time commitment of at least one person to each development would be essential if any real progress were to be made.

We therefore recommend the immediate appointment of a project leader for each class of data; he would have full-time responsibility for investigating requirements and developing systems so that a smooth take-over was possible on the creation of health boards and the CSA.

13. Patient identification

13.1. The influence of work on record linkage

Much interesting and valuable work has been carried out in recent years to improve the linking of medical records collected at different points of origin (15). The main point of immediate interest from this is that in Scotland a minimum of correctly recorded personal details such as surname, initials, date of birth, and sex (reduced by a Soundex code to a 14-digit ideogram), enable records to be linked correctly with a success rate which is more than adequate for statistical and research purposes (16). Thus records originating from a wide variety of locations and over a period of years can be linked successfully and this has enabled some research projects to be progressed satisfactorily on the existing fragmented sources of data.

Unfortunately, the necessity to link records for statistical and research purposes during a period when the NHS has been administratively divided has tended to obscure the need to link them for managerial and clinical purposes. For this purpose anything short of 100 per cent success may not be adequate. Broadly speaking, while epidemiologists have been developing techniques for their own purposes, clinicians, administrators, and patients alike have had to tolerate a system in which it was often difficult and sometimes impossible to retrieve and confidently match records for purposes of patient care.

13.2. Current argument

The value of retrieving previous medical records should be self evident and considerable attention is being given to uniform procedures of identification and filing within hospital groups. Moreover patient identification was one of the first subjects to which the SACCHS subcommittee on organization and interchange of data addressed itself. Some recognition of the true requirements has begun to emerge with the admission that use of the NHS number might ultimately be possible, but that the national ideogram would always be required as a supporting device and would remain the chief means for some time to come.

This seems to us a most unobjectionable point of view and the only real argument left is the time scale within which the NHS number might become widely used. Most people in a position to influence thinking incline to the view that it will not be possible to make universal or even widespread use of the NHS number before the 1980s: we consider that it could be brought into common use very much sooner.

13.3. The difficulties

There are at present some difficulties about the use of the NHS number for patient identification; the four main ones are:

a. Public attitudes to identification.

b. The unsuitable format of the NHS number.

c. The reluctance to use a common number throughout the NHS.

d. The difficulty of handling and refiling existing active records.

These do present practical problems which should not be underestimated; equally, however, they should not be regarded as insurmountable and in particular must be reviewed in the context of a unified health service.

13.3.1. *Public attitudes to identification*

There is a traditional British dislike of registration and identity numbers; only in time of war has there been any obligation to carry an identification card. An important consideration is that for all people in their early thirties and over the NHS number is their former wartime identification number and it is recorded on a dull buff card which closely resembles the identity card.

People will carry cards which enable them to gain access to facilities. Driving licences, credit cards, bankers' cards, union cards, work passes, or club membership cards are examples of cards which are carried regularly and we are convinced that there are no major problems in getting the public to carry a card for NHS purposes. Any such card will, however, have to satisfy the following conditions:

a. It must be attractive and modern in appearance.

b. It must be promoted as 'giving access' to NHS facilities rather than 'identification'.

c. It must be used by all branches of the NHS.

d. It must be the only card issued by the NHS.

The problem of convincing people of the necessity to carry their NHS card has undoubtedly obscured the extensive use which can be made of the NHS number whether they carry their card or not. Within the NHS itself there seems to be a belief that a patient must identify himself completely on every occasion. For the majority of cases this is not necessary. When a person visits his GP he is one of a comparatively small population and the GP can be expected to distinguish without difficulty even between two persons of the same name. Most visits to a hospital and most contacts with the local authority's health services are made on some sort of appointment or scheduled basis and receptionists know who to expect so that here again there is little or no problem. In cases of emergency or unscheduled attendance there are three levels of identification:

a. The patient can identify himself fully (because he is carrying a card or knows his NHS number) in which case there is no problem.

b. He or someone else can identify himself 'partially' (by name and address, perhaps also indicating whether he has attended that hospital before) in which case there is an indexing and retrieving problem.

c. He is unable to identify himself at all (for instance because he is unconscious and carries no identification papers of any kind), in which case no system is going to be of the slightest use.

Insufficient research has been done on public attitudes to identification for any firm conclusions to be drawn at this stage. The experimental work on card-carrying in Aberdeen (17) is interesting and provides one source of information for planning further work in this field. However, much more extensive experience of personal identification has been gained by the major clearing banks and the credit-card companies and the NHS could usefully consult such organizations.

13.3.2. The unsuitable format of the National Health Service number

In Scotland there are five different formats of mixed alphanumeric characters, one of which even has both upper- and lower-case alphabetic characters. The GRO is introducing a further variation, an all numeric number, for all new registrations from 1 January 1972.

Both patients and staff of the NHS are reluctant to use the existing numbers. The original 1939 format AAAA NNN (where A represents an alphabetic character and N represents a numeric digit) is reasonably easy to handle but nobody can fail to sympathize with those who have to deal with the format AA NN AN NNNNNNNN. The only satisfactory solution is to issue a revised NHS number to all the population, but the GRO, whose registrars issue the numbers on behalf of the NHS, have indicated that this would be a massive undertaking and that it would only be justified if they had a firm assurance that the new numbers would be used.

The 1972 format will be eight digits, three for registration district, two for year of birth, and three for a sequential number in the calendar year in each district. The number will obviously be suitable for computer processing but it would be easier to remember and still suitable for computer processing if part of it (the registration district) were alphabetic. While the systems recommended in this report could eventually reduce the necessity for transcribing or memorizing a common number, the necessity cannot be eliminated entirely and there is little doubt that people find car registration numbers and old telephone numbers much easier to remember than new all-figure telephone numbers.

It will, of course, be many years before numbers issued from 1 January 1972 form even 50 per cent of all NHS numbers, and some steps do need to be taken to make some of the existing numbers more suitable. We suggest that the format AA NN AN NNNNNNNN is by far the worst and should have immediate attention in any revision programme. There are some 2¼ million of this type of number: they could be revised by a straightforward computer program, which could also print all notifications to executive councils, doctors, and patients. The major effort would be in collecting the input and amending the executive councils' and doctors' records and we have discussed the need to do this for other purposes in Chapters 5 and 12.

13.3.3. The use of a common number

The majority of hospitals use a unique patient identification number in addition to name, sex, and date of birth for operational and administrative activities and at least one health centre is assigning patient numbers for filing and identification purposes. On the other hand the Scottish DEB does not use a number at all and it is only for the executive councils' doctors' lists that much use is made of the NHS number.

The continued proliferation of *ad-hoc* numbering systems is not conducive to an efficient system of record-keeping and record transfer, and is unsatisfactory in a society where there is increasing population mobility. The NHS must make a decision on the use of the NHS number; we recommend that it commit itself to a uniform policy of a common number for all purposes so that a suitable format can be established.

A complete commitment to a single identification number is in everyone's interest and is the only valid basis on which the GRO could justify the cost of revising and reallocating the NHS number.

13.3.4. *Handling and refiling of existing records*

This is a problem of changing existing practices and resembles in some ways decimalization, metrication, and driving on the right-hand side of the road. (The longer a change is postponed the more expensive it becomes.) It is, moreover, important to distinguish those environments for which a total change must be made at an appointed time, those which allow some period of changeover even though officially a new system is in force, and those for which two systems can continue in force indefinitely. Driving on the right of the road is obviously of the first type, decimalization of the second, and metrication of the third (how long will it be before all cookery books are revised?). Changing to use of the NHS number seems to us to be of the second type and it will require considerable effort to reorganize all active files and records over a relatively short period. Hospitals will be faced with the biggest task and some thought needs to be given to the possibility of aiding each hospital in turn to make a once and for all change, or of aiding all hospitals to make a simultaneous gradual change. (The latter implies changing each record to the new system on the next occasion it is used until the residual records are few enough in number to be tackled by concentrated effort.) The method chosen could vary according to the size of hospital and present method of dealing with records.

13.4. Conclusion

The difficulties associated with the use of the NHS number are not insurmountable. A lack of administrative cohesion and the tripartite structure have been a barrier to the introduction of a uniform system of patient identification. NHS staff do not like the format of the number, do not therefore use it, and do not therefore ask patients for it. The integration of the health services provides the opportunity to adopt a new approach and break this circle of circumstances.

The introduction of a satisfactory number and the commitment to use it exclusively is in everyone's interest. It puts patient identification where it belongs—at the point of contact between patient and the NHS. Record linkage both for operational (scheduling and care) and research purposes will no longer be a major problem and the use of ideograms can be restricted to their proper role of handling existing historical data and for the minority of cases where proper identification is not available.

Finally, no system can be designed to overcome the problem of the totally unidentified or deliberately obstructive patient. We must assume that the majority of people seeking medical treatment are willing and able to produce adequate identification. The level of co-operation by patients and the public in general will be influenced significantly by the national and local public relations activities—people will co-operate if they are told how to help and can see a smooth efficient system developing.

14. Public attitudes to databanks

14.1. The introduction of computers

Individually identified records are constantly in use for a very wide range of industrial, commercial, government, social, and medical purposes. As far as we can establish there is no specific legislation in force concerning the use, or limitations on use, made of such data. It has in the past generally been accepted that it is in an organization's own interest to maintain a satisfactory security system for storing such data and moreover to restrict use of the records, letting them be used only for mutually acceptable purposes (acceptable to the individual without putting undue restriction on the organization concerned).

There is no doubt that people regard their medical particulars as very personal and the accumulation of this data into large databanks which are more readily accessible than hitherto can lead to misgivings regarding the immediate and future use of such data. Few people have any clear idea of the use which is made of individual medical records, other than for patient care. Press reports on the 'misuse' of data can therefore be very damaging to public confidence. The Press report (18) on the National Morbidity Survey in England and Wales was an example of this. Referring to the doctors participating, it stated: 'They have not tried to secure their patients' permission because they were told that many were bound to refuse and the survey would then not be fully representative.' After further investigation a qualifying statement was issued (19) but the original article was bound to give rise to doubts in the public mind on the use made of data by official bodies.

The NHS and the medical profession are faced with a conflict of interests because patient privacy in the general sense is not directly compatible with efficient administration and detailed epidemiological studies. The Tunbridge Report (20) set out a basic code of practice and acknowledged in paragraph 11 that medical records would be of increasing importance as a source of data for management purposes. We consider that without any doubt the primary and secondary documents, or summaries of them, are an essential source of information for many purposes ranging from day-to-day administration through to operational research exercises.

The formation of computer-based databanks to replace manual handling of files and records is basically a rationalization of operational procedures and there can be no intrinsic objection to an organization such as the NHS adopting the new techniques.

The introduction of computer methods has, however, made it possible to process data much more rapidly; as a result there is greatly increased scope for its use and it can be made available to a large number of people in an organization. Equally important is the possibility of making large sets of individually identified records available to other organizations. The problems of security and confidentiality have therefore become much more serious.

Table 14.1. *Classification of records and their uses*

	Treatment	Management	Research
Collected records with no identification	No	Yes	Yes
Single records with no identification	No	No	Yes
Collected records with identification	Yes	Not necessary	Yes
Single records with identification	Yes	No	Yes

An indication of the serious nature of the problem is the existence of the Privacy Committee of the British Computer Society which has prepared a preliminary submission to the Younger Committee (21). This suggests the need for legislation to protect the individual and organizations against unauthorized and unwarranted intrusions into their privacy. Specific recommendations are mostly concerned with confidentiality and the right of individuals rather than what may be termed 'physical security', for instance of computer storage and computer terminals. The two aspects do indeed need to be distinguished and are discussed separately below.

14.2. Security
We consider security to be a relatively straightforward issue. The problems of physical security of data can be overcome, at a price. Operators of databanks will have to demonstrate physical security to the public if they are to retain public confidence and it may be necessary for each organization to appoint a security officer charged with the specific responsibility of developing standards of physical security and ensuring that they are met. Such an officer should be a computer expert. He would also need to be supported by legislation to ensure the availability of adequate penalties for deliberate violations of security against which it would be uneconomic to install safeguards.

14.3. Confidentiality
The problem of confidentiality is far more difficult, especially where medical records are concerned. A possible classification of records and their uses is shown in Table 14.1. Records without identification will not cause any worries over confidentiality and it may be assumed that patients are willing to accept the necessity for identification when they are having treatment. For all cases above the line, therefore, the problem to be overcome is the one of physical security discussed in the previous section. The major difficulty with regard to confidentiality arises in research work, where the identity of the patient is known. This is use of data for purposes other than those for which it was collected: it is at the very heart of the privacy issue.

If at the same time it is desired to add information collected outside the NHS, for instance by Social Work Services or the local Social Security offices, then the second element of controversy would be present—the linking of medical with non-medical data.

It is easy enough to state that data should not be used for purposes other than those for which it was collected and that medical data should be kept separate from other data. In practice however, this is likely to prove difficult since there will always be special cases which in the minds of some warrant bending of the rules. Furthermore, public opinion on what is acceptable and what is not changes with time, sometimes radically, and practice should always be enabled to reflect public opinion.

We do not consider there is any easy solution but a basis for development would be the appointment of an NHS 'licensing authority'. He need not be a computer expert but must be a person of acknowledged integrity. He would be responsible for considering those requests for access to individually identifiable records which lie outside publicly stated rules. Just as a security officer would need to be supported by legislation in order to be fully effective, a licensing authority would find a working code of practice helpful. The MRC published a code of practice in relation to experimental clinical procedures and a similar code of practice for medical databanks which is now being drawn up by that body would not only guide the licensing authorities, but would also help to allay public fears considerably.

14.4. Conclusion

An objective appraisal is needed of the purposes for which records must be explicitly identified. In parallel a much more detailed code of practice should be developed to set out policy on:

a. The use of patient data within the NHS.

b. Deciding who may have access to the data for both routine and special purposes.

c. The use of patient data for record linkage with other data from outside the NHS and the release of patient data to outside bodies.

The security officer and the databank licensing authority recommended in the previous two sections would have an important contribution to make to these developments and should be members of any committee which may be established to supervise the operation of NHS databanks.

The computer-based databank is a new concept which differs significantly from previous practice and much still needs to be done to evolve a form for working and control which is acceptable to the general public. The NHS and the medical profession must give a lead to developing a databank policy which sustains the public confidence they already enjoy.

15. Standardization

15.1. The National Health Service as a single entity

The NHS is a national service and there should be free interchange of ideas and information between regions, professions, and administrative branches of the service, and between the centre and the periphery leading to the adoption of common practices.

Unfortunately the present structure of the NHS has not been conducive to the development of standard methods of working and has led to each region developing its own payroll, each hospital its own record system, each laboratory its own methods, and each consultant his own waiting-list. Any attempts to standardize those procedures are now faced with established systems in which units and individuals have invested much time, effort, and money.

Standardization, however, should come to be regarded as selection of the best of many possible ways of dealing with a situation, establishing a minimum level of service to be provided or constructing a model of the highest degree at which all should aim. It should provide the springboard from which future developments can be made.

If the NHS is to make the best use of resources then the possibility of standardization of each procedure, whether clinical, nursing, administrative, technical, or ancillary, should be considered as soon as an acceptable way of carrying it out has been devised. This does not mean that no further developments will take place, but that developments will have a norm against which they can be measured. It will also be possible to regard developments as being of one of two types, first a development of the existing standard and second a radical new departure. Meanwhile all users will have something with which to work.

15.2. Standardization in information services

Nowhere is the necessity for standardization of basic work more apparent than in information services. The need for central direction of information services has been discussed in Chapters 3 and 11. The NHS is, in general, labour intensive and information services are no exception, whether they have a manual base which implies many clerical and statistical assistants, or a computer base which demands extensive software and application development. If the possibilities of the purpose-built training course and the cost advantages of bulk purchase of files and cabinets are to be realized, and the difficulties of obtaining comparable information from different sources other than by imposing a separate questionnaire are to be overcome then some degree of standardization has to be accepted.

For a computer-based system it is essential to be able to provide comparable information between health boards, from unit to health board and from health board to the centre. It is not sufficient to define the data which will be required at area or central levels since nobody can be sure what data may be required in one, five, or ten years' time. The way in which all data is held must be standardized so that any data which has been stored can be easily made available and if a new item of data is to be stored *all* areas and units will be able to cope with it.

15.3. The foundation

The possibilities and benefits of standardized administrative and clerical procedures are demonstrated clearly by the Drug Pricing Bureaux (DPB) and Dental Estimates Board (DEB) which have operated them successfully for a number of years. It is doubtful whether either of these bodies could function at all if 6,800 practitioners (2,700 doctors, 2,700 chemists, and 1,400 dentists) widely dispersed throughout the country had not agreed to use standard forms and standard methods of notation.

If either of these functions is more intensively automated full advantage will continue to be taken of the standardization so far achieved. This approach should be extended to other developments also and in fact the NHS could very usefully consider developments in industry and commerce in many cases. There is an outstanding illustration of this in the many separate developments which have been undertaken for school health, immunization, cervical cytology screening, and patient follow-up programmes which are all basically identical with health visitors' and meter-readers' schedules, planning of salesmen's rounds, and scheduled order processing of large distribution networks. The problems associated with the basic framework of this procedure have been solved for all makes and models of computers, and for many manual and semi-automated systems, and the NHS can therefore concentrate specifically on three facets of the procedure which may be unique to each environment:

a. The scheduling algorithm.

b. The actual operation (examination, immunization, and so on).

c. Any further action which may be required as a result.

Table 15.1 shows the various phases of the procedure for one commercial and four NHS environments. It shows clearly the large common areas, and the differences.

The scheduling algorithm itself may be a simple input after each contact, for instance of a number of days, weeks, or months; it may be an equally simple 'every three months', or it may be a fairly complex calculation, perhaps based on the results of the previous consultation.

Each of the five cases has the same requirement of reporting the results, though the results themselves are of a markedly different kind and in the case of the patient follow-up register could entail complex calculations.

The results then need to be compared with some norm or previous record in order to establish the precise action to be taken on exit from the procedure.

In three cases it is necessary to notify two separate people of the encounter that is to take place but this is not usually necessary for health visitor and meter reader who visit people in their homes, although it should be noted that the householder may require the meter reader to make an appointment.

Table 15.1. *A comparison of procedures for meter readers, health visitors, immunization, cervical cytology screening, and special patient follow-up registers*

	Meter readers	*Health visitors*	*Immunization*	*Cervical cytology*	*Specialized follow-up*
1	Schedule visit	Schedule visit	Schedule consultation	Schedule consultation	Schedule consultation
2	—	—	Notify patient	Notify patient	Notify patient
3	Notify meter-reader	Notify health visitor	Notify doctor or clinic	Notify doctor or clinic	Notify doctor or clinic
4	Read meter	Make visit	*a.* Carry out immunization *b.* Check results of, e.g. vaccination	*a.* Take smear *b.* Examine smear	*a.* Examine patient *b.* Get any test results required
5	Report readings	Report any special findings	Report results	Report results	*a.* Report results *b.* Evaluate results
6	Enter billing procedure	Take any further action required	Take any further action required	Take any further action required	Take any further action required
7	Update status for next visit	Update status for next visit	Update status for next consultation	Update status for next consultation	Update status for next consultation

15.4. The future

We have subjected the 'meter-reading procedure' to careful scrutiny because it highlights the necessity to make use of common procedures, programming, and systems wherever possible. The possibility of borrowing from previous work should have been obvious once the requirements of each job had been determined; the advantages of a common framework on which to hang individual requirements are that basic problems have been solved and those developing the application can concentrate their attention on items specific to the new environment.

A large data system for the entire health service of Scotland cannot be established if a large number of authorities undertake unco-ordinated developments. The word 'standardization' has become very emotive and the concept needs to be seen for what it is—a distillation of the best available knowledge and practice.

We discuss in Chapter 16 the need to ensure that data is captured accurately at the lowest cost possible and an important consideration in achieving this will be the adoption of standard forms and procedures. The adoption of standard forms and formats will be helpful in all cases where subsets of records emanate from difference sources and are subsequently merged. Particular examples are where several hospitals will be forwarding records to a health board and where health boards are forwarding data to some central agency. There is, of course, a need to adopt this procedure where individual records go directly to a common agency as has been recognized in the case of the DPB, DEB, the SHASC (form AR 1), and the SNSC (form SR 1).

The value of standardizing hospital medical records was urged strongly in the Tunbridge (20) and Walker (22) reports and it would be helpful if records used by GPs could be standardized to conform with those recommended for hospitals.

The need for standard methods of handling and processing data also requires attention. In particular the growth in the use of computers will necessitate standard processing software if costs are to be contained to an acceptable level. There is no merit in each health board (still less each hospital) undertaking individually the *ad-hoc* development of software packages for processing data which all boards will be handling. Duplication is always wasteful and time-consuming and it significantly reduces the rate at which a wider range of processing facilities can be made available to the NHS as a whole. An over-all assessment should be made of the need for processing facilities, common methods of processing should be agreed and each health board should undertake the development of an appropriate part of the total requirement.

Standardization does not necessitate the imposition of an inflexible system on the NHS. A system can retain sufficient flexibility to explore new avenues or incorporate modifications dictated by changing needs and the development of working methods.

15.5. Summary

The NHS should be in a position to produce standard systems which can provide a good basic level of service and allow individual units to pursue specific developments. These latter developments in turn could become part of the standard systems.

A number of developments will be found to have large common elements, and provision of standard methods for those elements will enable the NHS to concentrate on problems which are individual to each environment. It is often helpful to look outside the NHS to see what help can be gained from apparently unrelated exercises.

Unnecessary duplication of effort must be avoided in the future. Each health board should be asked to develop specific parts of the system, after a general assessment of methods and requirements has been made.

16. Data capture

Many people in the NHS are required to record data for their own future needs and as part of the process of communicating information to other branches of the service. Few people record data as their main working task.

Many people are required to study, interpret, assess, and act upon recorded data which may emanate from a variety of sources. The volume of data being recorded and transmitted is increasing and the NHS in common with many other organizations must undertake a very serious review of the cost and effort involved in data capture.

The wide variety of activities in the NHS call for varying degrees of accuracy in data recording and speed of communication for action and this prevents us from making blanket recommendations on a course of action. What does need to be done, however, is to ensure that each activity requiring the recording and transmission of data is subjected to rigorous and realistic examination to ensure that the data is captured economically, that is to say at a price worth paying in relation to its value. A fundamental aim must be to minimize the effort necessary to record data without loss in clarity, accuracy, and completeness and without impairing the speed of onward communication.

16.1. Appraisal of activities

Wherever possible data should be captured as a by-product of the activity it relates to and not as a separate exercise. There are already indications that this concept is being put into effect in isolated areas; in particular the SMR 1 and SMR M have been developed in some regions and hospitals to serve as a multipurpose document:

a. As a summary for the patient file.

b. As a diagnostic index for the consultant.

c. As a discharge notification to the patient's GP.

d. As the source document for central data processing.

This concept must we think be extended to other activities, but in doing so sufficient attention must be given to establishing certain basic principles relating to the activity concerned. They can be expressed in the following questions:

a. Why is the information recorded?

b. For what other purposes is the data to be used?

c. In what way is the data presented, to whom is it communicated and who is responsible for its transmission from one point to another?

d. What is the time-scale (response requirements) for the objectives to be achieved?

e. Is the effort and cost worth committing?

A good example is the processing of prescriptions originating from GPs. The primary objectives are:

a. To provide drugs to the patient.

b. To pay the chemist.

The secondary objectives are:

a. To examine the validity of doctors' prescribing habits—i.e. incidence of over-prescribing and prescribing of foodstuffs.

b. To examine the validity of claims for exemption from prescription charges.

c. To examine the over-all pattern of drug usage and cost.

The procedures associated with these objectives are summarized in Table 16.1, which could be the first step towards bringing together relevant information for activities such as prescribing so that a comprehensive picture of the capture and movement of data can emerge. The table provides a sound basis on which to examine and plan changes which may from time to time be introduced. Changes may range from improving the flow of data (in response time and cost) through to extending the use made of the data, and the table would help to identify the major areas of development required if, for instance, it were planned to introduce cost-related prescription charges.

Whilst this procedure is closely akin to systems analysis procedures we have deliberately avoided such terms so that there is no implied suggestion that computer data-processing is the only way of effecting improvements in data capture and flow. Indeed it is evident that much can be gained in speed and cost of data capture by O & M procedures which would not only be of immediate value but also facilitate the subsequent introduction of data-processing methods.

For an information record to be of maximum value, and thus justify the expense of its capture, it must be accurate, complete and be transmitted to the right place at the right time. Many systems have foundered through lack of attention to these points and it is worthwhile examining the main detailed considerations which require attention after the over-all appraisal of the activities has been carried out.

16.2. Accuracy

Accuracy is always a relative quality and in this case is dependent on the purpose for which the data is to be used. Errors are bound to occur and procedures must be devised to reduce them but there is a level of error beyond which further expense is not justified. To achieve accuracy, attention must be given to the source, environment, and attitude of personnel generating the data.

It is not practical to employ experienced specialist personnel for the preparation of the large mass of data which is the outcome of each day's work in a large organization. This is usually impossible if the organization is widely dispersed with a great variety in size and type of operating unit as is the case in the NHS. Dependence for accuracy must rest therefore on a large and diverse section of the personnel and they must be encouraged to appreciate the importance of correctly recording data at the time it is generated. Atten-

Table 16.1. *The use of form EC 10*

Objective	Preparation	Transmission	Cycle time
Drugs to patient	Free format by GP. Addition by patient for exemption	Individually by patient to chemist	Maximum 24 hours
Pay chemist	Free format addition by chemist	Batched by chemist to DAB	Monthly
	Pricing and sorting by hand. Totalled by chemist	Notification of totals to EC	Monthly
GP prescribing	Sorted by hand on sample	Notification to EC	Quarterly
Validity of exemption	Sort by hand for sample check	Notification to patient	Monthly
Pattern of drug use	Sort by hand (several). Punch on cards and process	Summaries to EC and SHHD. Listing to SHHD	Monthly Annual

tion is much more likely to be paid to accuracy if the supplier is himself dependent on the same data in some way in his day-to-day activities. Thus if a mistake is made about an employee's salary it will quickly be brought to light in the next payslip and the employee will ensure that it is put right. Similarly if a consultant supplies data about patients and receives in return an analysis of his activities which he uses in planning his future work, he has a vested interest in ensuring that the data he originally supplies is accurate. However, the key phrase here is 'which he uses in planning his future work' for it is obvious that the analysis supplied must be of current relevance. The turn-round period must therefore be short and this probably implies localized initial processing of data, whatever may be the scope of its ultimate use.

For prescription data there should be no great problem over accuracy since the doctor and the chemist both have adequate reasons to ensure accuracy, in the health of the patient and the payment for dispensing.

Interpretation and transcription also have an important bearing on the accuracy of data. In the design of pro-formas adequate space must be provided to record the required information. All too often one finds forms which provide the same size of box for surname and address; everyone will be aware of the gross inadequacy of space provided for employers' names and addresses on income tax returns. If the data has to be cramped up in the space provided, those completing the form will make arbitrary abbreviations, which can lead to errors in interpretation and transcription. Transcription itself provides an opportunity for error, causes delay in onward transmission of data and costs money. Data-processing and O & M personnel therefore lay great emphasis on capturing data at source in a directly usable form. A particularly interesting example of this practice is the EC 17 (Scotland) form used by dentists, developed jointly by SOCS and DEB; this serves all requirements as an on-going record including prior-approval, post-approval, costing, and ultimately as a historical reference.

16.3. Completeness

Items of information missing from a record can reduce the value of the record. Free format and narrative records can easily result in lost items of data because they provide no guidance to the person recording data. Forms requiring specific entries are preferable but here also guidance must be given to users so that blank boxes are reduced to the lowest level possible. It is always preferable to have the answer 'not known' or 'not available' rather than have no entry at all.

16.4. Timeliness

Data should be captured as it arises as monthly and weekly form-filling sessions can cause difficulty in tracing missing items. Batching of records for onward transmission must be judged in relation to the activity, but again a steady onward flow is preferable to annual or quarterly lumps. The personnel on the receiving end should have a steady flow to handle and may well need to make an up-to-date assessment based on the data available to them. In any case a quarterly or annual analysis will always be subject to delay if data for that period has to be handled in one batch.

This sort of problem is currently being experienced in the central analysis of in-patient data (SMR 1) for the SCRIPS project due to the batching policy adopted in some regions and some of the value to consultants is being lost by the time-lag between data receipt, processing, and subsequent distribution of analysis.

Manpower planning is an important activity which is also experiencing difficulties due to lack of sufficient up-to-date data. Much of the information available is eighteen months behind the current manpower position in the NHS and there is no doubt that this reduces the value of the work done in this important field.

16.5. Media available

While this study is concerned with data and information, and not with computers, it is obvious that a data system of the size and complexity required in the NHS is only feasible if computer facilities are available. It is reasonable therefore to devote a major part of any discussion on media to such devices as can be directly related to computer input.

The methods of data capture employed in any particular situation will depend on the environment and the procedures best suited to that environment. It is still common practice for managements installing a computer to pay scant attention to the area of data capture. Too often it is found at the eleventh hour that a substantial card-punching load has been created, and that special forms have to be designed in order to allow punching. Thus a two-stage transcription process is introduced, first on to punching documents and then on to cards.

In some circumstances the cards themselves are an inefficient computer input medium and direct entry to magnetic tape and magnetic disc has been developed in recent years to speed up the input process. It is claimed that the 'punching' process has also been speeded up by direct entry but of course the transcription via punching documents often remains.

Some pilot studies are now under way in the NHS where the user enters data directly on a visual display unit (VDU). In certain environments, this may prove very useful and the outcome of the experiments in progress is awaited with interest.

The greater part of NHS data-capture requirements can, however, be met by comparatively simple methods which are already well developed. The four main techniques are:

a. Turn-round documents.

b. Pre-punched cards.

c. By-product tape or cards.

d. Optical character recognition (OCR) or document readers.

Combinations of these techniques are possible. For instance, some manufacturers can supply an off-line document reader which produces paper tape while pre-punched cards are often used in a turn-round situation and a turn-round document is often fed into a document reader.

There are a large number of applications where turn round techniques can be applied. Immunization, cervical cytology screening, and other follow-up programmes are obvious examples in community care while hospitals can make extensive use of the technique for recording of attenders, defaulters, and next appointment at out-patient clinics, additions to and selection from waiting-lists and admissions.

Pre-punched cards can be used for ordering tests and recording significant events and discharges, as has been shown at the United Birmingham Hospitals and at hospitals run by the Assistance Publique in Paris. At Birmingham the cards are produced as a by-product of a typing process, but they could equally well be produced as a by product of a turn-round admission list.

Cards or paper tape produced as part of some other activity have always seemed attractive. Commercial firms have made use of the techniques both in connection with accounting machines used for ledger processes and with enhanced typewriters or flexowriters where mixed narrative and code are entered but only selected portions are converted to the punched medium. Both accounting machines and flexowriters can be easily programmed to provide extensive format control.

These devices may be useful in some areas of the NHS, for instance stock and purchase ledgers. The chief use of by-product media could, however, prove to be in transmission of patient details, particularly names, address, and NHS number between different members of the NHS, for instance doctor to pharmacist, doctor to hospital, hospital to doctor, and hospital to hospital. Details frequently have to be written or typed, or both, accuracy consequently being at a premium. If the patient's personal identification details could, for example, be embossed on a plastic card, only that single card would have to be accurate in order to achieve fast and accurate transfer of data.

OCR techniques have been used on an experimental basis for a variety of applications for several years but many potential users have reservations on the adoption of the available systems due to high cost and unreliability.

However, SOCS have made some interesting progress with the use of OCR in processing the results of the Scottish Certificate of Education Examinations. In 1970, 110,000 candidates' marks were transcribed by trained members of the Examination Boards staff for subsequent input by OCR. The results were encouraging and in 1971, 40 per cent of those who marked candidates' scripts entered the data themselves. They were given no training but were given a leaflet explaining how to write the figures for OCR purposes. This experiment was very successful and in 1972 all of those marking papers will be asked to complete forms in OCR format.

The four possible methods (turn-round documents, pre-punched cards, by-product cards and tape, and OCR) must always be considered in addition to traditional data preparation (card, tape, disc) at one extreme and highly sophisticated, expensive visual display techniques at the other. The most economical and most accurate means must be sought, and this will usually be the means most convenient to the user.

16.6. An integrated approach or a piecemeal approach?

We have observed during the study that there are significant overlaps in the current effort being directed at both routine data capture and the design of forms. Much of this has historical origins and is associated with the current tripartite structure of the NHS. However, we suggest that it is time for the whole question of uniformity of practice to be reviewed in its new context. Suitable arrangements need to be introduced to ensure a satisfactory degree of standardization in data capture within and between health boards. This must be balanced, however, to ensure that any *real* local needs can be catered for and that suitable arrangements are made to allow freedom to explore changing requirements which will emerge as the new structure develops. There is a great deal of work to be done in the NHS on efficient data capture, with limited resources of manpower and money: duplication of effort by piecemeal development must be avoided. Careful planning and delegation will be required to ensure that the maximum progress is achieved and we consider that it would be of value to examine whether the various health boards could undertake the study and development of data capture for specific activities as part of an over-all plan for subsequent adoption on all-Scotland basis.

16.7. Subsidiary data capture

The nature of medical care and administration is such that research and development form an intrinsic part of the routine activities and it is often difficult to draw a clear distinction between data which is captured in connection with routine activities and data which is specifically required for research investigations. More effort must, however, be made to identify how research requirements (emanating from the NHS and teaching hospitals) can be linked into the routine activities of patient care and NHS administration. Research work falls into the category of secondary objectives and must be viewed as such if the burden of data capture is to be kept to a tolerable level.

Because of the close ties between government ministerial activity and the NHS there is always a danger that special (and perhaps prolonged) data-gathering exercises may have to be undertaken to meet political requirements, for example reviewing the working of the Abortion Act. We are confident that most of these requirements could be met by retrieval of information from the databanks discussed in other sections of this report but the SHHD should give consideration to this in the planning of data gathering to meet statutory and parliamentary needs.

16.8. Summary

A large percentage of the expenditure on any systems development will be concerned with data capture. A systematic appraisal of requirements in each environment is therefore a sound investment.

Forms where used need to be designed with care. Capture and transfer of data should wherever possible be a flow process rather than a series of large infrequent batches.

All possible media should be examined but generally the simpler and cheaper the medium the more effective and acceptable it is likely to be to the users. Some simple techniques are well established and should be easily adaptable to NHS needs.

An integrated approach is required, where possible taking into account the need of research and government statistics, so that progress can be as rapid as possible.

17. Staffing and costs

Our terms of reference (see Appendix A) include an assessment of any special staffing requirements (item 2*d*) and the scale of costs and areas of savings (item 4*b*). Staffing requirements will be responsible for a major part of the costs of development and we have therefore decided to bring staffing and costs together in a single chapter.

First it must be clear that if the cost of introducing them is not to be prohibitive the data systems recommended in this report must replace rather than augment existing routine data collection and procedures. Throughout the NHS substantial manpower effort is devoted to collection, collation, and presentation of data; the same staff can provide data for an integrated information system equally easily.

There are two starting-points for the discussions in this chapter, first the recommendations in Chapter 11 of this report on organization of information services and secondly suggestions in the Green Paper (1) and the White Paper (2) that some specialized services in an integrated NHS might be uneconomic to provide in each area and would therefore be provided through co-operation between groups of health boards.

The number of groups can probably be decided empirically but it does not seem likely to us that there can be fewer than three, considering the geography of Scotland, and initially at least more than five would be something of a luxury. Although there might be some variation in size, each group would on average be responsible for an area with a population of about one million and an annual budget of about £35 million. We shall examine these figures for their implications regarding staffing and costs of information services.

17.1. Integration of information services

The necessity for a carefully planned development programme was outlined in Chapter 12 while other chapters have discussed problems of patient identification (13), standardization (15), and data capture (16). The extent of development work to be undertaken, the scarcity of staff, and the necessity to extract maximum value for all money spent all suggest that the maximum co-ordination between the different groups of health boards and between health boards and central bodies should be sought.

Consideration of the proposals in the White Paper (2), the contents of the report *Doctors in an Integrated Health Service* (23), and recommendations of various chapters in this report indicates that each group of health boards might at any time be able to employ up to three information systems development teams profitably. The first would undertake development work specially commissioned by the central information services group, the second would be engaged on systems development for the particular group of health boards, and the third would provide special services required by specialists in community medicine. In addition a maintenance team would be required to ensure that systems were kept up-to-date and latent errors removed as soon as they appeared. The composition of these teams would vary, but we envisage about twenty-five specialist systems staff in all.

The effectiveness of the information systems discussed in this report will be strongly influenced by the degree of user involvement in the development stages. In Chapter 11 the use of multidisciplinary teams was recommended and such teams will be required at the periphery also.

Selected staff from appropriate disciplines often working part-time or intermittently but sometimes seconded full-time to the project team have the vital role of ensuring that what is planned and ultimately implemented is of value in the working environment and actually does what the specific user groups require.

A wide range of NHS staff would therefore be required to participate in the development of information systems. A further examination of Fig. 5.1 which shows the activities centred on the master patient register will illustrate the point. To develop an effective register of this sort would require the participation of medical staff (from hospitals, general practice, and local authority health departments), nurses (both hospital and domiciliary), and administrative staff (from hospitals, including records officers, executive councils, local authorities, and the GRO).

17.2. Staffing of the central group

In Chapter 11 we discussed the organization of the information services group with two major divisions, namely research and statistics and data processing. The first is a well-established activity (although it may well increase in scope and hence require additional staff) so that the main concern in this section is staffing required for data processing.

The central group would require a strong team covering disciplines such as computer hardware, systems development, operations research, and organization and methods. This team would have a dual role, first provision of assistance and guidance to other central groups developing personnel, supplies, and drugs information systems, and secondly provision of expertise, direction, and co-ordination for the systems developments undertaken at health board and unit level. While staffing requirements of the central information services group cannot be quantified precisely at present, there are major systems in personnel, supplies, drugs, and buildings to be developed and maintained, and specialist leadership to be provided in hardware, software, and operations research. The application areas might need an average of 20 permanently assigned staff and the specialist services a further 20, making 100 staff in all.

As already emphasized above, multidisciplinary teams would be essential and we assume that no developments would be undertaken without active participation from user groups.

17.3. Costs

While it could be misleading to attempt a detailed estimate of all costs likely to be incurred on development of an information system, three major areas of costs can be identified and discussed. These are direct staffing costs (that is staff concerned with development of systems), equipment costs, and consequential staffing costs (that is staff required to operate the systems developed and equipment purchased).

17.3.1. Direct staff

Direct staffing costs can be calculated from the requirements postulated in sections 17.1 and 17.2 above. Five groups at the periphery each with a staff of 25 systems development specialists together with the central group of 100 make a total staff of 225. An average salary for a group of this calibre could be in the region of £2,500, giving an annual salary cost of £562,500.

17.3.2. Equipment

Each group of health boards would require computer facilities. Initially they would have to make use of whatever facilities were already available but the equipment may need to be resited, enhanced, or replaced to be of maximum use. The main activity would be centred on the patient registers of health boards, registers which for each group would contain one million entries with up to 300 characters per entry. Equipment to handle basic data of this order of magnitude could be obtained for perhaps £500,000 giving a total for health boards of £2·5 million.

Centrally there is an option between a single large installation on which to base all applications and a number of smaller installations, each dedicated to a particular application area. In either case the cost of hardware and initial software could be in the region of £2-2·5 million.

We therefore envisage a total capital cost of hardware in the region of £5 million; the systems developed would be far-reaching and it is suggested that the cost of hardware should for evaluation purposes be spread over a long period, perhaps as much as ten years. On this basis, annual costs of computer hardware would be £500,000.

17.3.3. Auxiliary staff

Development of systems and acquisition of hardware necessitate introduction of operations staff and data-preparation staff. Operation of each of the health board computer groups would require at least 9 operators, at 3 per shift, plus supervisory and control staff of whom there could be a further 9. For data preparation, however, much use is made of the various techniques described in Chapter 16 some specialist staff will still be required. We suggest 10 as a purely notional figure to deal with the workload at each group of health boards making 28 staff at each group or 140 staff altogether.

Centrally the need could vary substantially, depending on the number of systems which are installed and the manner in which they are co-ordinated, but a total staffing complement of about 100, probably equally divided between data preparation and equipment operation and control would probably be required. Total staffing requirements are therefore in the region of 240 and at an average salary of £1,500 annual cost would be £360,000.

17.3.4. *Total costs*

The total annual costs arrived at above are:

Direct staff	£562,500
Equipment (averaged over ten years)	£500,000
Consequential staff	£360,000
	£1,422,500

Our assumptions are broad and calculations approximate; technological advances can easily change the whole picture. Nevertheless the figure of about £1·5 million would be a reasonable first estimate on which to base future plans, a figure which represents less than 1 per cent of the annual budget of the Scottish health service.

It must be emphasized that these costs do not take into account equipment which may be installed and staff who may be employed at hospital level, but are purely those envisaged for managerial and administrative purposes at health boards.

As stated at the beginning of this chapter the same staff who now collect, collate, and present data will continue to provide data for an integrated system; we have therefore excluded data collection from our estimates of cost.

17.4. Savings

Any discussion of savings must be tentative. Running costs may rise, an increased volume of activity may mask comparisons with past performance, and the difficulties of redeploying staff or terminating their services mean that all potential economies are seldom realized. The tentative nature of the conclusions is especially true of the NHS, where any savings which do accrue are likely to be absorbed by provision of more extensive facilities. The biochemistry laboratory offers a good example of this process: introduction of autoanalysers and computers has not resulted in any reduction in total costs or total staffing but a large increase in throughput, lower cost per test, and a higher test/technician ratio have all been achieved.

The savings we are about to discuss may therefore never be realized in practice, because they may be converted into a more comprehensive service to the patient.

17.4.1. *Duplication*

a. Acheson (15) lists thirty-five different kinds of medical record which may be compiled about an individual. Some of these may not occur very often but one class of record which is in widespread use is the hospital case-note. In Scotland the number of new out-patients per year is over two million, each of whom has to be registered in the hospital files. As a minimum, patient details have to be recorded and checked, index cards have to be prepared and labels have to be printed. Acheson assessed the cost of this process at 30p (6s.) in 1967 based on figures provided in the Ministry's 1964 Hospital Costing Returns. A figure of 50p would not be excessive at 1971 values, on which basis registration procedures would cost in the region of £1 million annually. All the data required could be provided automatically from health board registers, and the 'registration' procedure for a new out-patient would then consist of checking that the data was still correct, and correcting any inaccuracies. Substantial savings could be achieved on this item and we tentatively suggest a figure of £500,000 although the difficulty of estimating costs in the first place makes discussion of savings on this item somewhat theoretical.

b. Some existing computer services would themselves be replaced by the new services for which we have included costs of staff and equipment. Costs of existing services are difficult to ascertain but figures obtained from one regional board suggest they must be at least £300,000 annually and likely to increase substantially. How much of the existing services can be replaced depends on the success of the integrated structure recommended.

c. Current inflation of doctors' lists, at 5 per cent or 250,000 people is costing the NHS £600,000 annually. If inflation were reduced to 1 per cent, savings of approximately £500,000 could be made on the present basis of capitation payments.

17.4.2. *Redeployment of resources*
It is difficult to quantify savings in this area but an efficient manpower planning service, leading for instance to lower staff attrition rates, could have a potential saving of up to 1 per cent. On staff costs of over £100 million, this would be worth £1 million. Such a saving would take a number of years to realize, and the methods of calculation would require careful examination.

17.4.3. *Reduction in consumption and stockholding*
Tighter controls and more advanced techniques should lead to economies in both consumption and stockholding.

Economies in consumption can be expected because of such possibilities as the feedback which can be provided to doctors on prescribing patterns and the reductions which can be made in wastage rates of foodstuffs or other perishable supplies. Economies in stockholding also result naturally from rationalization of product ranges and distribution points.

Use of advanced techniques has led to substantial economies in commercial and industrial concerns and it does not seem over-optimistic to expect savings of up to 5 per cent on drugs and general supplies bills. This suggests that savings could eventually reach £2 million annually.

17.4.4. *Total savings*
We have examined only a few areas where there is obvious potential for savings and our list is by no means exhaustive. One of the most important savings could prove to be in the actual operation of the new systems when compared with the costs of the present systems. (The Royal Air Force recently estimated (24) savings of 13 per cent on staffing costs of their computerized personnel databank compared with the previous manual system.) It is impossible to ascertain such savings in the NHS, however, because of the fragmented nature of many activities.

The total suggested on these basic areas is around the £4 million mark. The figures are tentative but are based on minimum expectations. We consider the greatest 'saving' will be the improved service that an integrated information system will make possible.

17.5. Conclusions

The number of staff envisaged and the annual cost of an information system may seem high, but should be viewed against the background of a very large organization employing 80,000 people with an annual budget of £180 million, moreover the benefits to be gained are substantial both in terms of service provided and possible cost savings.

Furthermore it must be remembered that the development of information services will be gradual (see Chapter 12) and that the NHS will not suddenly be faced with an increase of expenditure of £1·5 million. If developments are carefully planned increases in expenditure will not only be gradual but will soon be matched by corresponding increases in savings or in improved service. The Scottish health services would be well advised to take a long-term view of the problems to be solved; we consider the early establishment of forward plans to be a vital necessity.

Appendix A. Terms of reference

A managerial and administrative data system for an integrated health service

Preliminary study: Determination of an outline specification

Terms of reference

1. Information requirements

a. To ascertain what information is required for managerial purposes at national and health board levels.

b. To ascertain the frequency with which such information will be required, ranging from patient data to the annual presentation of statistical data.

c. To ascertain the urgency with which the information may be requested and/or required.

NB. 'Information' is used in the broad sense: it is not restricted to patient or medical data, but includes, for example, manpower data. It is not intended, however, to conduct a major review of financial and accounting information services.

2. Organization

a. To investigate the roles of SHHD, GRO, SOCS, SACCHS, and any other central bodies which are or might be established.

b. To investigate the roles of non-central authorities, taking into account the variability of size between otherwise similar bodies.

c. To investigate the advantages and disadvantages of various possible locations for central and other databanks.

d. To consider the implications of any special staffing requirements which may emerge from the investigation.

3. Operation

a. To recommend methods of data capture for the various environments.

b. To investigate methods of data transfer between locations.

c. To recommend means of information retrieval.

d. To indicate the minimum amount of standardization required, and the amount of variability which can be permitted.

e. To take account of the need for comparability of UK statistics.

4. Implementation

a. To make recommendations on the phasing of developments, with particular reference to the establishment of health boards and existing central and regional systems.

b. To indicate the associated scale of costs and those areas of existing activity where consequential savings may be expected.

5. *Public attitudes*

To highlight any problems regarding legal requirements, confidentiality, and public opinion which need to be overcome, with particular reference to interaction with other government departments.

Appendix B. List of those consulted during the study

1. Administrative divisions, professional groups, and individuals of the Scottish Home and Health Department

Division IIC. Local Authority Health Services
Division IID. NHS Executive Council Services
Division IIIA. Health Services Building
Division IIIB. Hospital Service Staffing
Division IIIC. Mental Health, Laboratory Services, Training, etc.
Division IIID. Superannuation and Hospital Supplies
Division IIIE. Research and Intelligence Unit
Division IIIF. Health Service Planning and Administration
Finance Division
Health Planning and Hospital Services Group
Medical Sciences Development and Education Group
Epidemiology and Environmental Health Group
General Medical Services and General Practice Group
Mental Health Group
Chief Medical Officer
Deputy Chief Medical Officer
Chief Nursing Officer
Chief Dental Officer
Chief Pharmacist
Chief Statistician

2. Other national or central groups

General Register Office for Scotland
Scottish Office Computer Service
Scottish Hospital Administrative Staffs Committee
Scottish Nursing Staffs Committee
Scottish Dental Estimates Board
Scottish Drug Pricing Bureau, Edinburgh

3. Officers and staff of regional hospital boards

Western Regional Hospital Board, Glasgow
South-eastern Regional Hospital Board, Edinburgh
North-eastern Regional Hospital Board, Aberdeen
Eastern Regional Hospital Board, Dundee
Northern Regional Hospital Board, Inverness

4. Officers and staff of hospital groups

Royal Infirmary, Glasgow
Glasgow Northern Hospitals
Royal Infirmary, Edinburgh
Royal Edinburgh Hospital
Edinburgh Southern Hospitals
Aberdeen Royal Infirmary
Ninewells Hospital, Dundee
Perth Royal Infirmary
Inverness Group of Hospitals

5. University departments not included under hospitals

Public Health and Social Medicine, Aberdeen
Joint Research and Intelligence Unit, Aberdeen
Pharmacy and Therapeutics, Dundee

6. Local authority services

Deputy Medical Officer of Health for Glasgow
Director of Social Work Services, Glasgow
Department of Social Paediatrics, Glasgow
Medical Officer of Health, Aberdeen County
Medical Officer of Health for Inverness County and Inverness Burgh

7. Executive council and general practitioner services

Executive Council for Inverness County
Grangemouth Health Centre
Craigshill Health Centre, Livingston
Group Practice Clinic, Lodgehill Road, Nairn
Royal College of General Practitioners Research Unit, Birmingham

8. Other bodies

Nuffield Provincial Hospitals Trust
British Petroleum Co. Ltd, Personnel Department

Appendix C. References

1. Scottish Home and Health Department (1968). *Administrative Reorganisation of the Scottish Health Services* (Edinburgh: HMSO).

2. — (1971). *Reorganisation of the Scottish Health Services*, Cmnd. 4734 (Edinburgh: HMSO).

3. Heasman, M. A. (1970). 'Scottish Consultant Review of In-Patient Statistics (SCRIPS)', *Scott. med. J.* **15**.

4. Todd, Lord (1968). *Royal Commission on Medical Education, 1965-68*, Cmnd. 3569 (London: HMSO).

5. Ministry of Health and Scottish Home and Health Department (1961). *Medical Staffing Structure in the Hospital Service* (London: HMSO).

6. Scottish Home and Health Department (1967). *Organisation of Medical Work in the Hospital Service in Scotland*, First Report of the Joint Working Party (Edinburgh: HMSO).

7. Ministry of Health and Scottish Home and Health Department (1966). *Report of the Committee on Senior Nursing Staff Structure* (London: HMSO).

8. Scottish Home and Health Department (1969). *A Study of the Work of Hospital Junior Medical Staff*. Scottish Health Service Studies no. 10.

9. — (1969). *Nursing Workload per Patient as a Basis for Staffing*, Scottish Health Service Studies no. 9.

10. — 'Report of the Working Party on Hospital Supplies Organisation in Scotland.' Departmental circulation.

11. Council for Scientific Policy, University Grants Committee (1966). *A Report of a Joint Working Group on Computers for Research*, Cmnd. 2833 (London: HMSO).

12. Scientific Control Systems Ltd (1968). *Commodity Coding—Its Effect on Data Recording and Transfer* (Manchester: National Computing Centre).

13. Management Services (O & M) Division (1968). *Pricing Prescriptions by Computer-Feasibility Study*, CSD Ref. 2OM818/293/01 (unpublished).

14. Ockenden, J. M., and Bodenham, K. E. (1970). *Focus on Medical Computer Development* (Oxford University Press for the Nuffield Provincial Hospitals Trust).

15. Acheson, E. D. (1967). *Medical Record Linkage* (Oxford University Press for the Nuffield Provincial Hospitals Trust).

16. Report (1969). 'Record Linkage Conference', *Hlth Bull.* **27**, no. 3, 31.

17. Innes, G., and Weir, R. D. (1968). 'Patient identification on a regional basis', in McLachlan, G., and Shegog, R. A. (eds), *Computers in the Service of Medicine* (Oxford University Press for the Nuffield Provincial Hospitals Trust).

18. Article (7 December 1970). 'Health secrets snoop', *Daily Express*.

19. Article (19 December 1970). 'Keep names secret order in health probe', ibid.

20. Ministry of Health, Central Health Services Council (1965). *The Standardisation of Hospital Medical Records*, Report of the Sub-Committee of the Standing Medical Advisory Committee (London: HMSO).

21. Privacy Committee of the British Computer Society (1971). 'Submission of evidence to the Committee on Privacy', *Computer Bull.* **15**, no. 5, 169.

22. Scottish Home and Health Department and Scottish Health Services Council (1967). *Hospital Medical Records in Scotland—Development and Standardisation* (Edinburgh: HMSO).

23. — (1971). *Doctors in an Integrated Health Service*, Report of a Joint Working Party appointed by the Secretary of State for Scotland (Edinburgh: HMSO).

24. Article (1971). 'Dramatic cost savings at RAF databank', *Computer Weekly*, **233**, 12.

Appendix D. Bibliography

General

Department of Health and Social Security (1970). *The Future Structure of the National Health Service* (London: HMSO).

Ministry of Health (1959). *Final Report of the Committee on Cost of Prescribing* (London: HMSO).

— (1967). *Report of the Committee of Enquiry into the Relationship of the Pharmaceutical Industry with the National Health Service, 1965/67,* Cmnd. 3410 (London: HMSO).

Article (1970). 'OCR checks doctors' over-prescribing', *Computer Weekly Internat.* 3, 13.

Crooks, J., Clark, C. G., Caie, H. B., and Manson, W. B. (1965). 'Prescribing and administration of drugs in hospital', *Lancet*, i, 373-8.

Office of Health Economics (1964). *The Cost of Medical Care* (London: Office of Health Economics).

Scottish Regional Hospital Boards (1970). *Scottish Hospital Costs* (year ended 31 March 1970).

Databanks and information retrieval

Patterson, R. (1967). 'IR and road accident statistics', *Computer Bull.* 11, no. 2, 123.

Herbert, E. (1966). 'Information transfer', *Internat. Sci. and Technol.* 51, 26.

Cuadra, C. A. (ed.) (1966). *Annual Review of Information Science and Technology*, vols. 1, 2, and 3 (New York: J. Wiley).

Montijo, R. E. (1967). 'California DMV goes on-line', *Datamation*, 13, no. 5, 31-6.

Davies, A. M. (1969). 'Towards a medical data bank for a total population', ibid. 15, no. 11, 257.

Warner, M., and Stone, M. (1970). *The Data Bank Society* (London: Allen & Unwin).

North Thames Gas Board (1971). 'An ambitious billing system becomes successful', *Data Management*, 3, no. 2, 6.

Hansard (House of Commons) (16 April 1970).

Hansard (House of Commons) (16 December 1970).

Hedley, A. J., *et al.* (1970). 'Computer-assisted follow-up register for the north east of Scotland', *Br. med. J.* 1, 556.

Data gathering

Townley, Helen (1967). 'Information coding techniques', *Sci. Business*, 2, 39.

Scottish Home and Health Department (1968 rev.). 'Scottish Cancer Registration Scheme' (Edinburgh, unpublished).

Raphael, Winifred (1969). *Patients and their Hospitals* (King Edward's Hospital Fund for London).

Murnaghan, J. H., and White, K. L. (eds) (1969). 'Hospital Discharge Data. Report of the Conference on Hospital Discharge Abstract Systems', *Medical Care*, 8, no. 4, Supplement (Warrenton, Virginia: J. B. Lippincott Co.).

Scottish Home and Health Department (1970). *Channels of Communication*, Scottish Health Service Studies no. 11.

Manpower

Young, A., and Almond, G. (1961). 'Predicting distributions of staff', *Computer J.* 3, 246.
— (1965). 'Models for planning recruitment and promotion of staff', *Br. J. Indust. Rel.* 111, 301.
Duffett, R. H. E. (1969). 'A quantitative approach to company manpower planning', *Manpower and Appl. Psychol.* 3, no. 1, 11.
British Petroleum Co. Ltd (1967). 'Manpower trends. Bulletin 2—The computer and personnel data' (unpublished).
— (1968). 'A guide to manpower planning' (unpublished).

Statistics

Heasman, M. A. (1968). 'Scottish Hospital Inpatient Statistics—sources and uses', *Hlth Bull.* 26, no. 4, 10.
Scottish Home and Health Department (1968). *Scottish Hospital In-Patient Statistics, 1966* (Scottish Home and Health Department).
— (1969). *Scottish Health Statistics, 1967* (Edinburgh: HMSO).
Ashford, J. R., and Pearson, N. G. (1970). 'Who uses the health service and why?', *Jl R. statist. Soc.* series A, 133, part 3, 295.